Professional Pilot's Study Guide
Volume 1

Piston Engines and Supercharging

Professional Pilot's Study Guide Volume 1

Piston Engines and Supercharging

Mike Burton

Airlife
England

Copyright © 1991 Mike Burton

First published in the UK in 1991
by Airlife Publishing Ltd

British Library Cataloguing in Publication Data
A catalogue record of this book is available from the British Library

ISBN 1 85310 273 3

Printed in England by Livesey Ltd, Shrewsbury SY3 9EB

Airlife Publishing Ltd
101 Longden Road, Shrewsbury SY3 9EB

Contents

1

AIRCRAFT PISTON ENGINES

1.1   Classification of Aircraft Piston Engines.

The layout or cylinder configuration of aircraft piston engines take
many forms. Fig.1-1 shows some of the layouts of engines that may be
used.

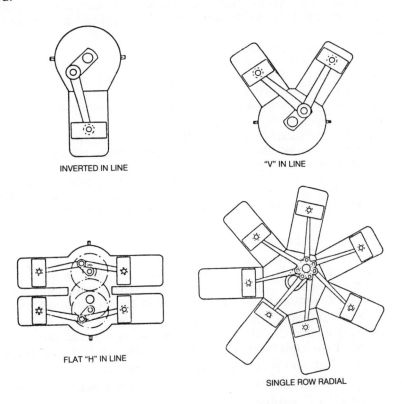

INVERTED IN LINE   "V" IN LINE

FLAT "H" IN LINE

SINGLE ROW RADIAL

Fig.1-1. Cylinder Arrangements.

It is usual to classify a piston aero engine by its method of cooling and
the arrangement of its cylinders, for example, air cooled radial; liquid
cooled in line; etc. Engines may be further classified by stating
the number of cylinders, whether aspirated or supercharged or
turbocharged.

1.2 General Functional Description.

Functionally, any piston engine consists of the following systems or sub-systems:

(a) Mechanical System.
   For converting the heat of combustion into power and consists of the cylinders, pistons, connecting rods, crankshaft, propeller shaft, etc. The pistons convert the combustion pressure to torque which is transmitted to the propeller either by direct drive, or through a reduction gear assembly.

(b) Lubrication System.
   Ensures the efficient lubrication of all moving parts. The work wasted in overcoming friction is thus reduced, and the heat generated by friction kept within reasonable limits.

(c) Cooling System.
   For dissipating excess heat and maintaining effective control of engine temperature; either air or liquid being used as the cooling agent.

(d) Carburetted Fuel System.
   To supply a correct fuel/air mixture to the cylinders. The correct mixture is ensured by metering the fuel, by means of a carburetter or injector, in proportion with the amount of air induced into the engine. The induction system directs the mixture to the cylinders.

(e) Ignition System.
   To ignite the induced charge. The fuel/air mixture within each cylinder is ignited by two spark plugs. High tension voltage, generated by two magnetos and distributed to the sparking plugs, producing the spark at the plug points. The ignition system is controlled by ignition switches; when the switches are in the 'OFF' position, the magnetos are rendered inoperative and the engine will not run.

1.3 Build up of an Engine.

All aero engines are made up of units and sub-assemblies arranged for convenience of dismantling, rig testing, and assembling. Each unit has provision for its assembly to its parent sub-assembly, which has similar provisions for assembly to the crankcase or to another sub-assembly.

The layout of sub-assemblies making up an engine, and the number of them varies considerably, according to the engine type etc, but general layout, taken from front to rear, for a geared supercharged is as follows:

(a) Propeller shaft and reduction gear assembly.

(b) Crankcase, which houses the crankshaft and connecting rods etc.

(c) Supercharger assembly.

(d) Wheelcase or rear cover assembly, on which are mounted the magnetos, various fuel and oil system components, and other accessories.

(e) The cylinders mounted on the crankcase; either individually or in blocks depending on the design of the engine. In addition to the above assemblies, a front cover is interposed between the reduction gear assembly and the crankcase to house the valve operating mechanism. The carburettor or injector is normally mounted on the rear of the engine.

1.4 Engine Mounting.

Aircraft piston engines are normally attached to the airframe via an engine bearer assembly. The engine bearer is then attached to the front bulkhead of the aircraft fuselage, in the case of a single engined aircraft, or engine bulkheads in the case of engines that are mounted on the wings.

The bulkhead not only serves as a mounting point for the engine but also provides a fire resistant wall between the engine and the cockpit or area behind the engine. Fig.1-2 shows an example of the engine bearer and wall or bulkhead.

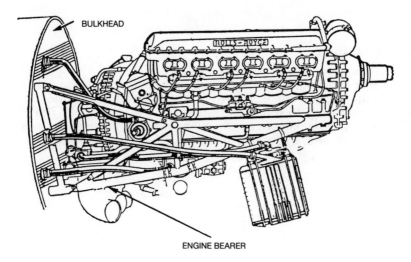

Fig.1-2. Engine Bearer and Bulkhead.

2

FOUR STROKE PISTON ENGINES

PART ONE: BASIC PRINCIPLES

2.1 Introduction.

The internal combustion engine consists basically of a cylinder closed at one end, a piston, which slides up and down inside the cylinder, a connecting rod and crank by which reciprocating movement of the piston is converted to rotary movement of the crankshaft. The closed end of the cylinder, known as the cylinder head, includes an inlet and exhaust valve, and a sparking plug. Fig.2-1 shows the basic arrangement of a single cylinder.

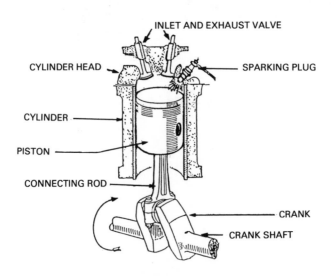

INLET AND EXHAUST VALVE

CYLINDER HEAD

SPARKING PLUG

CYLINDER

PISTON

CONNECTING ROD

CRANK

CRANK SHAFT

Fig.2-1. The Basic Components of the Piston Engine.

The purpose of the piston engine is to convert heat energy into mechanical energy, the conversion being accomplished by burning fuel in the cylinder, and utilising the pressure of combustion to work the arrangement of piston, connecting rod, and crankshaft.

2.2 The Four Stroke Cycle.

The sequence of operations, by which the heat energy is converted into mechanical energy, is known as the four stroke cycle. A mixture of fuel and air, known as 'the mixture', is drawn or induced into the cylinder, the mixture is compressed, and, when at maximum compression the mixture is ignited, the heat generated caused a rapid increase in pressure which drives the piston down the cylinder. This operation can be divided into four separate, but mechanically related, operations. These operations are normally referred to as INDUCTION, COM-PRESSION, POWER and EXHAUST.

2.3 Principle of Operation.

The basic principle of operation of the four stroke engine is as follows:

(a) Induction. (See Fig.2-2).
   During the induction stroke, the inlet valve is open, and the piston is descending down the cylinder thereby causing a drop in pressure resulting in the mixture being drawn into the cylinder through the inlet valve. The power output of the engine depends on the weight of mixture induced into the cylinder or cylinders.

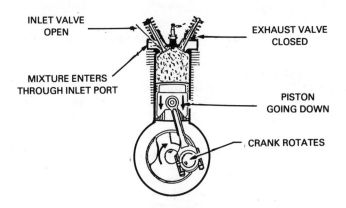

Fig.2-2. Induction Stroke.

(b) Compression. (See Fig.2-3).
   As the piston completes its induction stroke, it now starts to move up the cylinder. The inlet valve closes and the mixture is compressed. By compressing the mixture into a smaller space, the pressure it exerts when burnt is proportionally increased.

   When the piston is at its lowest point of travel (i.e. maximum space in the cylinder) it is known as being at Bottom Dead Centre (BDC). When the piston is at its highest point of travel (i.e. minimum space in the cylinder) it is known as being Top Dead Centre (TDC).

The ratio of the cylinder volume, when the piston is at BDC, to the cylinder when at TDC, is known as the COMPRESSION RATIO. It should be noted that this is a ratio of volumes, and not a measure of increase of pressure in the cylinder. As the mixture becomes compressed, it is heated adiabatically, as well as by conduction from hot surroundings, the pressure consequently rises to a higher value than that to be expected from volumetric reduction alone.

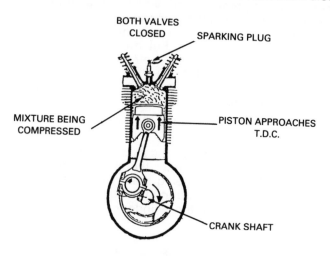

Fig.2-3. Compression Stroke.

(c) Power or Ignition. (See Fig.2-4).
A spark at the sparking plug ignites the compressed mixture and combustion causes a rapid expansion of gas pressure in the combustion chamber. As both valves remain closed, the increased gas pressure forces the piston down in the cylinder.

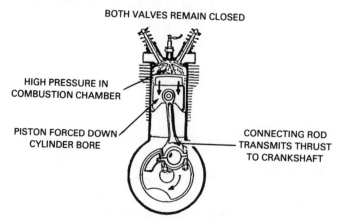

Fig.2-4. Power Stroke.

Note: As the piston is forced down the cylinder the gas temperature will reduce.

(d) Exhaust. (See Fig.2-5).
The exhaust valve opens and the piston ascends causing the gases, now at a much reduced pressure, to escape past the open exhaust valve into the exhaust manifold and hence to atmosphere.

INLET VALVE CLOSED-EXHAUST VALVE OPEN

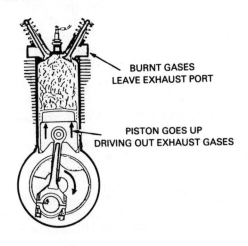

BURNT GASES
LEAVE EXHAUST PORT

PISTON GOES UP
DRIVING OUT EXHAUST GASES

Fig.2-5. Exhaust Stroke.

2.4 The "Otto" Cycle.

The basic principle of the four stroke cycle explained in paragraph two of this chapter is termed the "Otto" cycle, named after Dr. N. A. Otto who built the first successful engine working on the four stroke cycle in 1876.

2.5 Practical Application of the "Otto" Cycle.

It is important the inlet and exhaust valve open and close at the correct time to ensure efficient operation of the engine. In the theoretical four stroke cycle explained in paragraph 2.2 these requirements are met by admitting mixture through the inlet valve orifice from TDC to BDC, and expelling the burnt gases through the exhaust valve orifice from BDC to TDC, but practical considerations necessitate a slight departure from this timing.

2.6 Valve Timing.

The diagrams in Figs.2-5a & b illustrating the four stroke cycle show that the opening and closing of the inlet and exhaust valves is related to the position of the piston in the cylinder and hence the position of the engine crankshaft.

(a) Inlet Valve.

Early opening of the inlet valve ensures that the valve is fully open on the induction stroke, there is then no time lag between the piston moving down and the mixture flowing into the cylinder as would otherwise occur due to the inertia of the mixture. The inflowing mixture is therefore able to keep up with the descending piston. The momentum of the mixture increases as the induction stroke progresses, and towards the end of the stroke, is such that the gases will continue to flow into the cylinder even though the piston has passed BDC and is moving upwards a little. The closing of the valve is therefore delayed until after BDC when the gas pressure equals the gas pressure in the induction manifold. By allowing such a delay in closing the inlet valve, the maximum possible weight of charge is induced into the cylinder.

See Figs.2-5a & b

(b) Exhaust Valve.

Towards the end of the power stroke, the temperature and pressure of the burnt gases has decreased, the crank angle becomes less effective, and little purpose would be served in keeping the exhaust valve closed until BDC. It is advantageous, however, to open the exhaust valve before BDC and use the residual gas pressure to commence the scavenging operation before the piston starts moving up the cylinder. This reduces back pressure on the piston during the exhaust stroke when it has to push the gases out. The valve will close a little after TDC as the gas will continue to flow out due to its momentum − even after the upward movement of the piston has ceased.

See Figs.2-5a & b

(c) Valve Overlap.

There is a period during which both valves are open at the same time, this is known as "VALVE OVERLAP". During this overlap period, the action of the exhaust gases flowing out of the cylinder tends to reduce the gas pressure in the induction manifold. The mixture in the induction manifold commences to flow into the area of low pressure and assists in displacing the remaining burnt gases.

See Figs.2-5a & b

(d) Effective Ignition and Valve Timing.

   (i)   The limit to the speed of opening and closing of valves, beyond which excessive stresses would be imposed on the operating gear.

   (ii)   When a valve is almost closed mixture flow is minimal.

   (iii)   Time lag beween ignition and the build up to maximum pressure.

There are two periods during one crankshaft revolution, when the piston movement is very small, when little work is done in either induction, or exhaust. These periods occur when the crank is within the range known as the INEFFECTIVE CRANK ANGLE shown in Fig.2-5a.

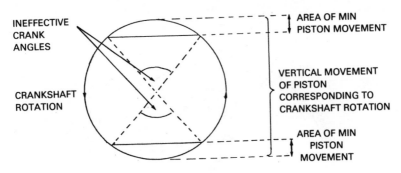

Fig.2-5a. Crank Angles.

These two periods offer a suitable opportunity for the valve operation, without excessive speed, and following the compression stroke, the mixture may be ignited before TDC, so that the maximum pressure build up is realised at the early part of the power stroke.

The practical timing, is as shown, and can be followed using Figs.2-5a & b.

(e) Ignition Timing.

Ignition is so timed to advance as the engine speed increases to ensure adequate burn time is provided for the mixture in the cylinder. Equally as engine speed reduces the ignition is retarded. It must be noted the spark even in its fully retarded position will occur before top dead centre.

Study Fig.2-5b.

Induction. The inlet valve opens before TDC of the exhaust stroke, and remains open during some 70° of the compression stroke. This delay, or **valve lag**, is to enable the momentum of the mixture to increase the weight of charge, thus increasing volumetric efficiency.

Compression. On the compression stroke, the spark occurs before TDC to allow the build up of pressure from the burning charge to reach maximum early in the power stroke, this is known as **ignition advance**.

Power. Before BDC on this stroke, the exhaust valve opens (**valve lead**). This allows pressure scavenging of the combustion chamber (cylinder).

Exhaust. As can be seen, the exhaust valve remains open until some 30° into the induction stroke, this is known as **valve overlap**. The partial vacuum left in the cylinder, by the rapid exit of the burnt gases, induces the fresh charge to enter.

2.7 Piston Engine Components.

Aero engines are generally made up of units and sub-assemblies,

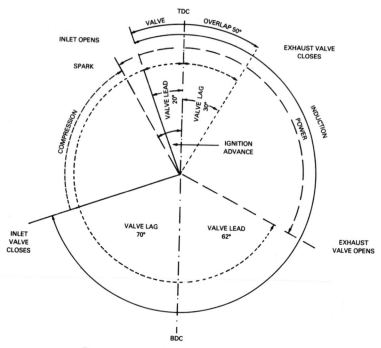

Fig.2-5b. Ignition and Valve Timing.

arranged mainly for the convenience of dismantling when replacement and/or rectification becomes necessary. The number of units, or sub-assemblies, varies with the type of engine, but a general lay-out is as follows:

(a) Engine block, housing, cylinders, pistons, valves and valve gear operating mechanisms.

(a) Crankcase, housing crankshaft and connecting rods.

Other units comprise components dealt with in following chapters.

2.8 The Cylinder.

The cylinder forms the combustion chamber, and provides a working bore for the piston. Although considered as one unit, they are in fact in two sections, the cylinder barrel, and the cylinder head, the latter being bolted, sealed air tight to the former. The cylinder barrels are usually made of steel, and may have a hardened bore, to increase their resistance to the wear of the piston. Cylinder heads are usually made of a light alloy – aluminium – primarily for lightness of weight, and heat conductivity. The head also comprises the valve seatings, and valve guides to form a bearing for the valve stems. The seatings are made of material strong enough to withstand constant hammering of the valves, and the corrosive action of the exhaust gases. Threaded inserts, of a more durable metal, are fitted to take the spark plugs. The cylinder head also supports valves and rocker gear, and sometimes the camshaft and drive. To facilitate cooling, the head may be finned for air cooling, or fitted with a cooling jacket, for liquid cooling. Cooling is dealt with in a separate chapter.

2.9 The Piston.

The piston (Fig.2-1) forms a solid gas-tight plug in the cylinder, and is made of a forged aluminium alloy to increase strength, and for lightness in weight and head conductivity. Due to higher linear expansion of aluminium, pistons are tapered slightly towards the crown, to enable parallel operation (to cylinder wall) at operating temperatures. The crown of the piston may be shaped to suit the cylinder and to give valve head clearance. Pistons are fitted with piston rings (gas rings) fitted into the piston ring grooves to maintain a gas seal between piston and cylinder, the rings being made usually of cast iron, which retains its springiness at high temperatures, and due to its low coefficient of linear expansion, only a relatively small "gap" is required. The rings when new, have a slight taper of the face which contacts the cylinder, giving a rapid initial wear, allowing the ring to wear to the bore quickly and does away with "running in". Another type of ring fitted is the scraper ring, which prevents an excessive amount of oil passing from crankcase to combustion chamber. Scraper rings are designed in various sections according to the action required – heavy or light; it is usual to have a single action ring on the skirt allowing some oil to pass to the thrust face of the piston, and a double action scraper, above the gudgeon pin for final heavy scraping. As can be seen in Fig.2-6 pistons are formed with bosses to accept the gudgeon pin, linking the connecting rod to the piston. Gudgeon pins "float" inside the piston for even wear, being retained by circlips. They are made of steel, and are hollow, thus increasing rigidity and the bearing surface of the small end, without strength decrease for the same cross-sectional area. On multi-cylinder engines, pistons are of the same weight, to ensure balance, and elimination of vibration.

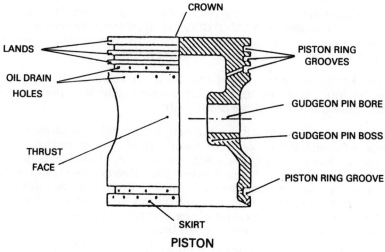

PISTON

Fig.2-6. Piston Assembly.

2.10   Valves.

Valves (Fig.2-7) open or close the gas ports, and may be one of two types, sleeve valves, or poppet valves. Sleeve valves take the form of a ported sleeve, moving within the cylinder wall. The more common type used is the poppet valve, which is made of special alloy steel, of great strength at high temperatures, non-scaling, and resistant to corrosion. The exhaust valve may be sodium filled, which assists in valve head cooling.

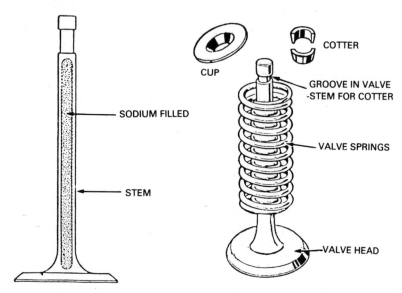

Fig.2-7. Poppet Valves.

2.11   Valve Gear Construction and Operation.

As can be seen in Fig.2-8 the valves are operated by what is collectively termed the valve gear, a detailed drawing of which is shown in Fig.2-9. The valve operating mechanism is driven by the engine crankshaft through a cam, push rod, and rocker arm assembly.

It should be noted at this point that as each valve opens only once during the four stroke cycle, through gearing reduction the camshaft rotates at half the speed of the crankshaft.

As can be seen from Fig.2-8 the opening of the valve is carried out by the rocker forcing the valve stem down against the resistance of the valve spring. The closing of the valve is a function of the valve spring as pressure by the rocker is reduced. When the valve is fully closed and the rocker is in its fully up position note there is a gap between the top of the valve spring and the rocker, this gap allows for expansion during the full operating temperature range of the engine and oil from the engine lubrication system to lubricate the two faces.

Normally valve springs are duplicated by fitting one spring inside the other, although this has a certain safety value should one spring break

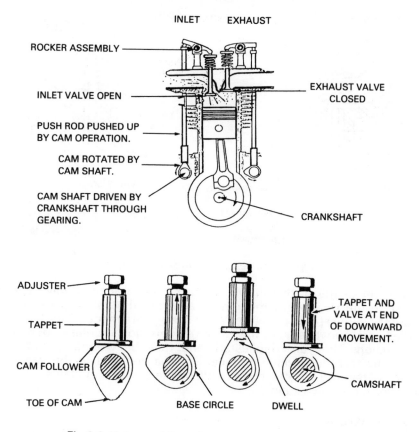

INLET   EXHAUST

ROCKER ASSEMBLY

INLET VALVE OPEN

EXHAUST VALVE
CLOSED

PUSH ROD PUSHED UP
BY CAM OPERATION.

CAM ROTATED BY
CAM SHAFT.

CAM SHAFT DRIVEN BY
CRANKSHAFT THROUGH
GEARING.

CRANKSHAFT

ADJUSTER

TAPPET AND
VALVE AT END
OF DOWNWARD
MOVEMENT.

TAPPET

CAM FOLLOWER

CAMSHAFT

TOE OF CAM

BASE CIRCLE   DWELL

Fig.2-8. Valve and Cam Operation on Induction Stroke.

whilst the engine is operating, their primary function is to reduce valve bounce.

The exhaust valve is subjected to very high temperatures and to assist in its cooling during normal operation it is manufactured with a follow stem which is partially filled with sodium.

The valve operating mechanism consists of, camshaft or a cam drum, tappets, push rods and rocker arms. As can be seen in Fig.2.9, the profile of the lobe of the cam controls the period in crankshaft degrees of opening, the rate of opening and the lift of the valves. Camshafts always run at half engine speed. In direct contact with the cams are the tappets, these being kept in contact by means of the valve springs. The tappets alter the eccentricity of the cam, into a reciprocating motion, this motion being transferred to valves by the push rods, and rocker arms. Play is always present when the tappets are on the "dwell" of the cam, which will ensure valves positively closing (by valve spring action). The play is known as tappet clearance. The rocker arms are pivoted centrally on a lay shaft, one side being in contact with the push rod, whilst the other side with the valve stem base. Thus "upward"

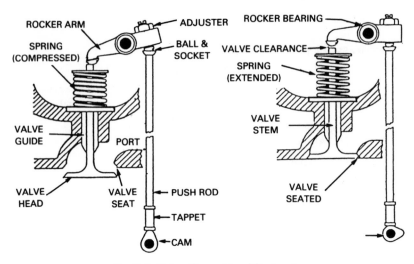

Fig.2-9. Valve Operating Mechanism.

movement of the push rod will open the valve against valve spring pressure, the downward movement allowing the valve to be closed under the same spring pressure. Valve springs are made of spring steel, and as seen above, ensure the valve remains closed unless opened by cam action. They are duplicated, and may be wound in opposite directions to reduce valve bounce. Springs are held to the valve by means of tapered colletts, fitted between the spring and plates, and the grooves in the valve stem.

2.12 Crankcase.

The crankcase forms the backbone of the engine being made of light alloy for weight and conductivity, and also being a single, or multi-section construction dependent on engine type. The crankcase houses the main bearings for crankshaft support, also forming the support for the cylinders. Main bearings may be plain or roller type, dependent on engine type – plain with in line, roller with radial. The crankcase also provides support for front and rear casings, supercharger, sump and reduction gears etc., as required.

2.13 Crankshaft.

See Fig.2-10. The crankshaft changes piston reciprocating movement, into rotary motion. They are alloy steel forgings and may have hardened crankpins and journals for wear. Classified according to the number of cranks it has, a shaft with one crankpin is termed a "single throw" shaft, with six crankpins a "six" throw. Fig.2-10 shows a "four" throw crankshaft. Drives at each end of the shaft transmit the rotary motion (torque) to the propeller, and the accessory drives (magnetos, oil and fuel pumps etc.). Aero engine shafts are usually hollow, making for a stronger, lighter shaft with large bearing surfaces of long life, the bore being a convenient passage for lubrication purposes.

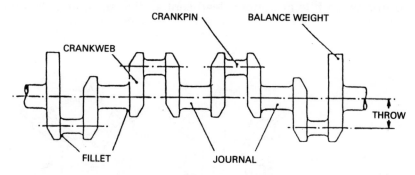

Fig.2-10. Four Throw Crankshaft.

2.14 Connecting Rods.

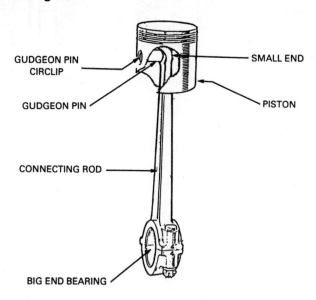

Fig.2-11. Connecting Rod.

See Fig.2-11. Link the gudgeon pin (and thus the piston) to the crankpin (thus to the crankshaft), transmitting the force of the piston to the crankshaft. They are usually made of H section alloy steel forgings, the girder section increasing resistance to bending and compressive loads. The rod may be of "one" piece when a built up crankshaft is used, but are usually found to have a split big end bearing with a 'cap" secured by bolts. The big end may be lined with anti-friction metal forming the bearing on the crankpin, with the small end bushed with bronze, forming the bearing for the gudgeon pin.

2.15 Swept Volume and Clearance Volume.

The compression ratio of a cylinder is equal to the total volume above the piston when it is at bottom dead centre, divided by the clearance volume when the piston is at the top dead centre. The difference between these two volumes is the piston swept volume. Fig.2-12 shows an example of this in practical terms.

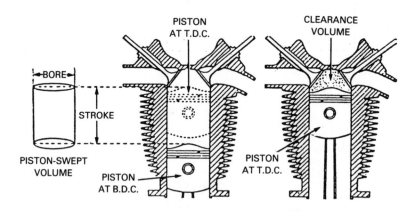

Fig.2-12. Swept and Clearance Volumes.

TEST YOURSELF 2
FOUR STROKE PISTON ENGINES

1. The valves of a four stroke piston engine will each:
   (a) open twice during the normal "Otto" cycle.
   (b) open once during the normal "Otto" cycle.
   (c) open four times during the normal "Otto" cycle.
                                               Ref. Ch 2 Para 11.

2. The camshaft of a piston engine normally rotates:
   (a) at twice the speed of the crankshaft.
   (b) at half the speed of the crankshaft.
   (c) at the same speed as the crankshaft.
                                               Ref. Ch 2 Para 11.

3. Tappet and rocker arm clearance is essential:
   (a) to allow lubrication between the contact surfaces.
   (b) to allow for valve operation by the cam.
   (c) to allow for expansion throughout the working temperature range of the engine.
                                               Ref. Ch 2 Para 11.

4. Valve "Dwell" is:
   (a) the period a valve remains open.
   (b) the period a valve remains closed.
   (c) the period taken by the rocker to take up the clearance gap before operating the valve.
                                               Ref. Ch 2 Para 11.

5. Valve overlap occurs:
   (a) at the end of the power stroke.
   (b) at the end of the exhaust stroke.
   (c) at the end of the induction stroke.
                                               Ref. Ch 2 Para 6.

6. The weight of charge induced into a piston engine cylinder during normal operation:
   (a) is increased by closing the exhaust valve before TDC.
   (b) is reduced by closing the inlet valve after BDC.
   (c) is increased by delaying the closing of the inlet valve.
                                               Ref. Ch 2 Para 6a.

7. The exhaust valve of a piston engine:
   (a) normally has a hollow stem partially filled with sodium.
   (b) is normally manufactured from metallic sodium to assist with cooling.
   (c) normally has a hollow head filled with sodium.

   Ref. Ch 2 Para 11.

8. Valve springs are primarily duplicated to:
   (a) to ensure a gas tight seal when the valve is closed.
   (b) to prevent the valve dropping into the cylinder in the event a spring breaks.
   (c) to reduce valve bounce.

   Ref. Ch 2 Para 11.

9. When the piston of a four stroke piston engine is toward the end of the power stroke:
   (a) the gas temperature will be at its highest.
   (b) the gas temperature will be reducing.
   (c) the gas temperature will remain constant until BDC.

   Ref. Ch 2 Para 6.

10. The compression ratio of a piston engine is the:
    (a) ratio of the cylinder volume when the piston is at BDC to the cylinder volume when at TDC.
    (b) difference in pressure generated when the piston is at BDC to that generated at TDC.
    (c) variation between the volume of the combustion chamber and the swept volume.

    Ref. Ch 2 Para 3b.

3

PISTON ENGINE LUBRICATION

Introduction.

3.1 Lubrication is a means of reducing friction and wear. Friction is the resistance to movement when one surface slides over another. Wear is the loss of material as a result of the two surfaces sliding together. Solid surfaces are never smooth, the actual contact between two sliding surfaces being limited to a number of high spots. When the high spots on a sliding surface are spaced well apart the material may be torn away; where the particles are very small the faces will become smoother but where large particles are affected the surfaces may become rough and smooth. The purpose of a lubricant is to prevent sliding surfaces from actually touching each other and thus to eliminate friction and wear. Any substance placed between two moving surfaces to reduce friction may be termed a lubricant; mineral oil is used as the normal lubricant for piston engines. The two methods of application are:

(a) Film Lubrication.

(a) Boundary Lubrication.

3.2 (a) Film Lubrication. A thin but measurable film of oil is maintained between the two surfaces and prevents them from touching. This film works in three distinct layers, the outside layers clinging to the two separate surfaces and the central layer moving between them. The thinner the oil the easier will this movement take place, the thicker or more viscous the oil the greater the force that will be required to move one surface on the other. If the oil is squeezed from between the surfaces the cushioning function of the oil is less effective and wear will become excessive.

(b) Boundary Lubrication. This is the state of near breakdown of lubrication where the film thickness has, by reason of load or loss of viscosity, been reduced to almost nothing. The surfaces, while not actually touching, are very near to it, but they continue to slide until the oil disappears.

Lubricant Requirements.

3.3 The properties which a lubricant should possess will vary according to the particular purpose for which it is to be used. All lubricating oils for piston engines are required to:

(a) "Wet" the surfaces to be lubricated.

(b) Possess a viscosity suitable for high loading and speeds, over a wide temperature range.

(c) Have a low evaporation rate at normal engine running temperature.

(d) Protect surfaces against corrison.

(e) Have a low gum or sludge formation rate.

(f) Be non-injurious to materials they contact.

Lubrication System.

3.4 Introduction: There are essentially two main types of lubrication systems fitted to piston aero engines.

(a) Dry Sump Lubrication System.

(b) Wet Sump Lubrication System.

Both types operate in a similar manner and fulfil the same basic function. The differences will be discussed later. The majority of aircraft piston engine lubrication systems are of the dry sump type. The following text refers primarily to a dry sump lubrication system.

Principle.

The internal moving parts of an aero-engine are lubricated by oil which is circulated from a tank in the airframe to the engine and back again by engine driven oil pumps. Far more oil is circulated by the pumps than is needed to reduce friction alone; the increased flow is used to cool the internal components of the engine. An oil cooler fitted in the return line to the tank dissipates the excess heat absorbed by the oil in its passage through the engine. The engine pump delivers oil under pressure

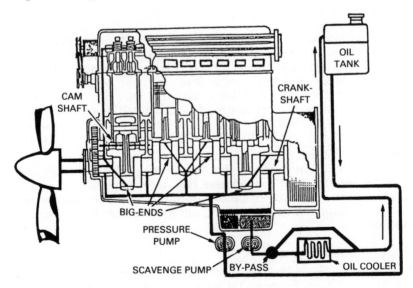

Fig.3-1. A Dry Sump System.

through internal ducts, hollow shafts and pipes to the main bearings, fitted to the engine. Oil escaping from these bearings is used to 'splash' lubricate ball and roller bearings, gears and other moving parts; where more positive lubrication is necessary, 'jets' of oil are directed onto the contacting faces. Oil in the engine drains into a sump where a scavenge pump passes the oil back to the tank.

3.5 Most lubrication systems with engines using plain main bearings have the oil delivered to them at fairly high pressure (60psi to 70psi), the oil then passes into the hollow crankshafts where ducts in the crankwebs and crankpins direct it to the big-end bearings. Oil escaping from these bearings is flung onto the cylinder walls, piston and gudgeon pins to provide splash lubrication. Other plain bearings in the engine, which are not so heavily loaded, are often fed with oil from an auxiliary circuit at a much reduced pressure. This auxiliary circuit is fed from the main system, the reduced pressure being controlled by a relief valve.

Operation.

Dry Sump Type.

The system comprises:

(a) Oil tank.
   This is normally a separate tank, mounted adjacent to the engine, which contains a reserve of oil to allow for minor leakage and provides an air space above the oil to allow for expansion and frothing.

See Fig.3-2.

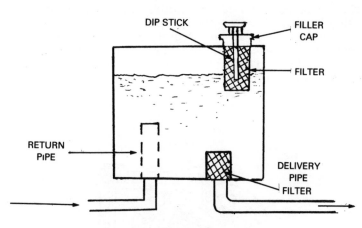

Fig.3-2. Oil Tank.

(b) Pressure Filter.
   As the oil is drawn from the tank, by the action of the pressure pump, it passes through the pressure filter to ensure clean oil is delivered to the engine.

See Fig.3-3.

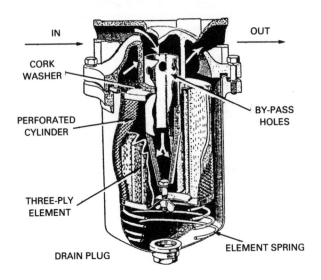

Fig.3-3. Pressure Filter.

(c) **Pressure Pump.**
   The pressure pump is normally of a spur gear type and is driven by the engine. It is designed to deliver a greater quantity of oil than the system actually requires, the surplus oil being used as a cooling agent for many of the engine components. A relief valve is usually fitted adjacent to or as an integral part of the pump assembly to relieve excess pressure on the outlet side of the pump. The relieved oil may be directed back to the oil tank or more usually back to the inlet side of the pump.

See Fig.3-4.

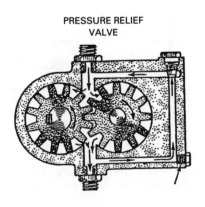

Fig.3-4. Pressure Pump.

(d) Delivery.

Oil under pressure is delivered to various jets and drillings strategically positioned in the engine to lubricate such components as main and auxiliary bearings, rocker gear, camshaft, cylinder walls and numerous other components.

See Fig.3-1.

Note: Aero engines fitted with superchargers and turbochargers utilise the engine lubrication system to lubricate the main bearings of such assemblies.

(e) Sump.

Engines fitted with dry sump lubrication systems utilise the sump as a form of collector tank. As the oil is allowed to drain from the components it has lubricated, it drains into the sump where it is then collected by the scavenge pump.

See Fig.3-1.

(f) Scavenge Pump

The scavenge pump normally has a greater pumping capacity than the pressure pump, to ensure that all oil is removed or 'scavenged' from the engine. Oil collected by the scavenge pump is drawn through a scavenge filter which removes any particles in the oil before it passes through the pump. The scavenged oil at this stage is very hot so is passed to a cooler.

See Fig.3-1.

(g) Oil Cooler.

Oil coolers are normally of the air cooled variety in that the oil is pumped by the scavenge pump through a matrix and is cooled by ram air being allowed to pass through the cooler in a similar manner to the radiator of a car.

See Fig.3-5.

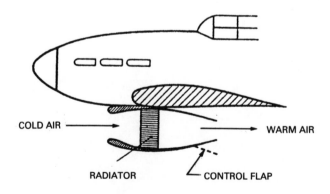

COLD AIR ⟶ ⟶ WARM AIR

RADIATOR   CONTROL FLAP

Fig.3-5. Oil Cooler.

(h) By-Pass.

Many modern piston engines are fitted with a by-pass valve which when starting the engine, particularly at low temperatures, allows the oil cooler to be by-passed thereby allowing the oil and the engine to reach normal working temperature more quickly. The by-pass valve is usually thermostat controlled.

See Fig.3-1.

Note: In most cases the pressure pump and scavenge pump are one assembly driven by a common drive shaft. Both pumps are of similar design with the scavenge pump having a greater capacity than the pressure pump.

Operation.

3.6 Wet Sump Type: Wet sump lubrication systems are rarely used on modern aero piston engines. Generally, the wet sump system consists of the same components as the dry sump with one major difference, that being: the sump of the wet system not only collects the oil as it drains from its lubrication points, but also serves as the oil tank and so the wet sump system has no separate oil tank. The major disadvantage of the wet sump system is that when the aircraft is inverted the oil is allowed to drain from the sump to the cylinders reducing the efficiency of splash lubrication, and could starve vital bearings of oil whilst the aircraft is in this attitude.

TEST YOURSELF 3
PISTON ENGINE LUBRICATION

1. The majority of aircraft piston engine lubrication systems are of the:
   (a) self lubricating type.
   (b) wet sump type.
   (c) dry sump type.
   Ref. 3.4.

2. A dry sump lubrication system:
   (a) maintains a reserve of oil in a separate tank.
   (b) maintains a reserve of oil in the sump.
   (c) requires no reserve of oil.
   Ref. 3.5.

3. The pressure pump of a dry sump lubrication system:
   (a) has a greater capacity than the scavenge pump.
   (b) has less capacity than the scavenge pump.
   (c) is driven on a common shaft and has the same capacity as the scavenge pump.
   Ref. 3.5.

4. The pressure filter in a dry sump lubrication system is:
   (a) located between the pressure pump and tank.
   (b) located after the pressure pump.
   (c) located between the scavenge pump and the tank.
   Ref. 3.5.

5. The by-pass valve of a dry sump lubrication system is:
   (a) normally activated during low temperature engine starting.
   (b) normally activated during high temperature engine starting.
   (c) is a relief valve excess oil pressure.
   Ref. 3.5.

6. Normally on most piston engines the lubrication oil of a dry sump system is cooled:
   (a) on leaving the pressure pump.
   (b) before returning to the oil tank.
   (c) before returning to the sump.
   Ref. 3.5.

7. The reserve of lubricating oil of a wet sump piston engine is stored in:
   (a) the sump.
   (b) a separate tank.
   (c) the pipe system.

   Ref. 3.6.

8. The oil tank of a dry sump lubrication system has a space above the oil to provide for:
   (a) jack ram displacement.
   (b) pressurisation.
   (c) expansion of the oil and frothing.

   Ref. 3.5.

9. A relief valve is provided to relieve excess pressure on:
   (a) the outlet side of the pressure filter.
   (b) the outlet side of the pressure pump.
   (c) the inlet side of the scavenge pump.

   Ref. 3.5.

10. The oil cooler of a dry sump lubrication system is normally cooled by:
    (a) water.
    (b) compressor air.
    (c) ram air.

    Ref. 3.5.

4

PISTON ENGINE IGNITION

4.1 Introduction.

Piston engines, other than compression ignition engines, depend on electrical ignition systems to ignite the mixture in the engine cylinders. The mixture is set alight by producing an electric spark at the gap between two electrodes positioned in the cylinder when it is desired to fire the charge. The initial flame on a gas turbine engine is started in a similar manner.

Two types of ignition system are in common use, coil ignition and magneto ignition. Coil ignition is used widely on motor cars and aircraft ground support equipment, generally its electrical supply is obtained from batteries or from a separate generator. The magneto which is always used on aircraft piston engines, is a self contained unit with its own built in generator.

4.2 Electricity.

Electricity is a form of energy and its pressure may be shown in one or more of the following ways:

(a) Heating Effect.
A flow of electricity generates heat in the conductor through which it flows. This effect can be seen in the hot element of an electric fire and in the glowing filament of an electric lamp.

(b) Chemical Effect.
A flow of electricity can cause a chemical change. For example when charging a battery the current changes the chemical composition of the plates and acid.

(a) Magnetic Effect.
A flow of electricity along a conductor causes a magnetic field to be set up around the conductor. If the conductor is wound into a coil a more powerful field is produced since the loops of the wire act together. This principle is used to form a temporary magnet which may be used for example, to attract the hammer of a bell and for relay and solenoid switches.

4.3 The Electrical Circuit.

Study Figs.4-1 and 4-2 in conjunction with the following text.

The conditions that exist in a simple electrical circuit can be compared with those in a water system as shown in Fig.4-1. The pump is the source of energy that, when the cock is open, water is directed under pressure on to the turbine so causing it to rotate.

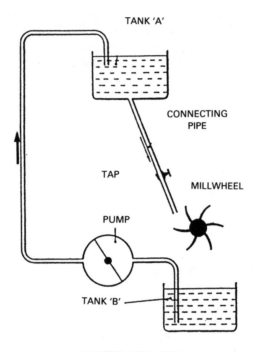

WATER ANALOGY

Fig.4-1. Water Analogy.

A simple electrical circuit is also shown in Fig.4-2. The circuit consists of a generator connected by conductors to a switch and a lamp. Here, the source of energy is the electrical generator that produces a difference in electrical pressure (known as voltage) between the positive and negative terminals. On closing the switch, which is the counterpart of the cock in the water system this voltage causes an electrical current to flow from the generator through the conductors and lamp back to the generator.

The heating effect of the current flow causes the lamp filament to glow and so produce light.

In the water system the resistance to the flow of water depends on the cross sectional area of the pipelines, their length, and their internal roughness. Similarly, in an electrical circuit the conductors resist the flow of electrical current. This opposition to flow (termed resistance and measured in ohms) depends on the cross sectional area of the conductors, their length, and the material from which they are manufactured.

Where the material is a good conductor, i.e. has low resistance more current flows for the same electrical pressure. Copper is a very good conductor and is widely used for this reason. To keep the resistance in a circuit as low as possible conductors must be large in cross sectional area, short in length, and of suitable material. Materials with an exceptionally high resistance to the flow of electricity are called "insulators"; examples are glass, porcelain, mica, rubber and some types of enamel.

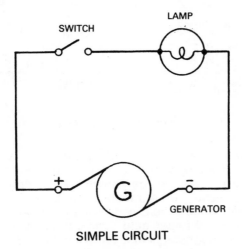

SIMPLE CIRCUIT

Fig.4-2. A Simple Electrical Circuit.

In the water system the rate of flow depends on the pressure created by the pump, i.e. the difference between pump outlet and pump inlet pressures. Similarly, in an electrical circuit the flow of current (measured in amperes) depends on the difference in electrical pressure or voltage between the positive and negative terminals of the generator.

4.4 Magnets and Lines of Force.

A magnet has an affinity for iron and this becomes apparent by the following effects:

(a) The ends of the magnet attract pieces of iron and steel. The ends, where the power of attraction are greatest, are known as the 'poles' of the magnet.

(b) If a bar magnet is freely suspended at its centre it comes to rest in the direction of the earth's magnetic field. The pole then lying nearest to the north pole is known as the north seeking or 'north pole of the magnet' the other is the south seeking or 'south pole'.

(c) If a second magnet is held near a pole of the suspended magnet the latter is either attracted or repelled according to the polarity of the magnet brought to it; like poles repel, unlike poles attract.

Fig.4-3 shows the effects of the magnetic lines of force on a bar magnet.

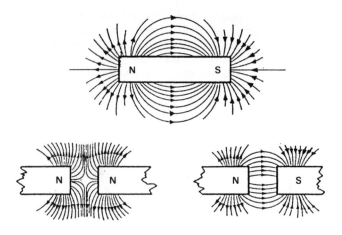

Fig.4-3. Lines of Magnetic Force.

The strength of the attraction present at the poles varies between magnets. Some indication of the area and strength of the field of attraction around a magnet can be shown by drawing lines of force. These show the direction of attraction and by their numbers, the intensity of the field. Such a field can be demonstrated by sprinkling iron filings on a sheet of paper held over a magnet. A diagrammatic representation of the magnetic field is shown in Fig.4-3.

Lines of force tend to deflect from their normal direction to pass through any magnetic body placed within the magnetic field. Advantage is taken of this fact in the design of electric motors, generators and magnetos.

A magnet may be either a permanent or an electro-magnet. The permanent magnet, which is made of a special alloy or steel, retains its magnetisim over a period of years provided it is carefully handled. The electro-magnet consists of a soft iron core with a number of turns of insulated copper wire wound around it. When an electrical current is passed through the wire the core becomes magnetised and remains so for as long as the electrical current is flowing, but, as soon as the current is switched off the core loses its magnetism.

Soft iron is used for the core because it is easily magnetised yet loses its magnetism very quickly when the magnetising force is removed.

4.5 Production of Electricity.

Electricity can be produced in a variety of ways, the more common methods being by expending chemicals or by converting mechanical energy.

(a) Expending Chemicals.
   If two dissimilar metals are immersed in certain chemical solutions or pastes, a voltage difference occurs between the two metals and, if they are connected by an external conductor electrical current flows. Such an arrangement is known as a simple cell. A simple cell

has a limited output but is of use with electric torches, door bells, and similar small units. Several cells connected together form a battery.

(b) Converting Mechanical Energy.

If an electrical conductor moves in a magnetic field so that it cuts, or is cut by, lines of magnetic force a voltage is produced across the ends of the conductor. This relative movement can be produced either by:

(i)   Moving the conductor across a stationary magnet field.

(ii) Moving the magnetic field across a stationary conductor.

(iii) Varying the strength or intensity of a stationary field about a stationary conductor. Such a variation has the same effect as the lines of force cutting across the conductor. See Fig.4-4.

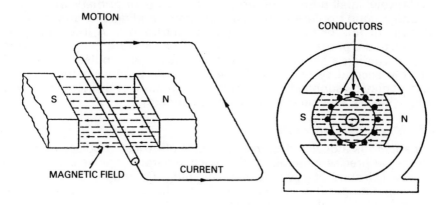

PRINCIPLE OF DYNAMO

Fig.4-4. Principle of Electricity Generation.

The strength of the voltage so induced into the conductor depends on the intensity of the magnetic field and the speed of the relative movement. The more intense the field and/or the faster the relative movement the greater is the amount of electricity induced.

An electrical generator, or dynamo, normally consists of a magnetic field that surrounds a rotating member, which carries the electrical conductors. Fig.4-4 shows a simple conductor moving across a magnetic field and the principle when applied to a generator.

4.6 Electro-Magnetic Induction.

It has already been stated that where a coil wound around a soft iron core is carrying a current, then a magnetic field, that remains as long as a current is flowing, is formed around both the coil and the core. If the current flow is stopped however, the magnetic field collapses and the lines of force move rapidly in towards the coil causing a current to be induced in any conductor that lies within the field. Similarly, a current is induced in such a conductor during the build-up of a current in the coil.

Consider two coils wound on an iron core, one above the other and insulated from each other. If a steady current is flowing through one of the coils a steady magnetic field is formed around both coils and the core but, because there is no relative movement between the lines of force and the second coil, a current is not induced into the second coil. If, however the current in the energised coil is cut off, the magnetic field immediately collapses and, cutting across the turns of the second coil, induces a current into it. This current flows for just as long as the magnetic field takes to collapse.

The voltage so induced into the second coil depends on the ratio between the number of turns in the first and second coils, the speed at which the lines of force collapse across the second coil, and the resistance of the final circuit.

Applying this principle in order to supply a series of sparks to an engine a relatively small number of turns of stout wire, or primary winding, is wound around the core and has a secondary winding of a large number of turns of fine or thin wire superimposed upon it. A low voltage is applied to the primary winding and by starting and stopping the current in this winding a series of high voltage electrical impulses is induced into the secondary winding. The low voltage producing the primary current may be supplied by a battery (coil ignition) or by incorporating a simple electrical generator in the unit (magneto).

4.7 Magnetos General.

A magneto is a device design to produce electrical impulses one after another at precise intervals so that each separate impulse can be used to provide a spark at a cylinder sparking plug. The magneto does this by first generating a low voltage and then collapsing the magnetic field created by the resultant current across the secondary winding to induce a high voltage impulse. A precise interval is essential to obtain correct ignition timing on all cylinders during engine running.

4.8 Description.

The essential components of a magneto are:

(a) A permanent magnet, which provides the magnetic field necessary to be able to generate a low voltage in the primary winding.

(b) The Primary, and the Secondary windings mounted on a soft iron core; the complete assembly is then known as the Armature.

(c) A rotating member that effects a change of magnetism on the armature. The particular basic principle used in the operation of the magneto is governed by this member and is indicated by the type name of the magneto, e.g. Rotating Armature Magneto, Rotating Magnet Magneto.

(d) A contact breaker assembly which is a mechanically operated switch timed to break the primary circuit when the maximum current is flowing.

(e) A condenser, which is connected across the contact breaker points. The action of the condenser, by reducing arcing at the contact breaker points when the points are open, stops the flow of primary current more quickly and thus brings about a faster collapse of the primary magnetic field. Further, by reducing arcing at the points, excessive burning and erosion of the points is avoided.

(f) The distributor, which directs the high voltage impulses to the cylinders in turn as they reach their ignition point.

The internal wiring of a magneto can be conveniently divided into two, the primary or low tension circuit, and the secondary or high tension circuit.

Primary Circuit.
A simple primary circuit is shown in Fig.4-5. It consists of a primary winding on a soft iron core, a contact breaker and a condenser. The condenser is connected across the contact breaker points.

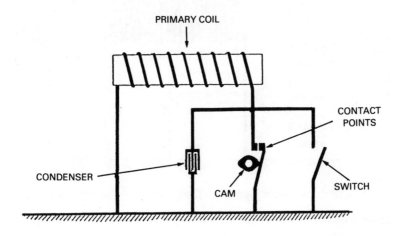

Fig.4-5. Primary Circuit.

The earthing switch shown is not a magneto component but is included to explain its action. Reference to Fig.4-5 shows that if the switch is closed the primary circuit is completed and the contact breaker action has no effect on the circuit. The magneto is therefore 'dead' when the switch contacts are together, and 'alive' when the switch contacts are apart, that is to say, the reverse of normal switch.

Secondary Circuit.
Fig.4-6 shows the secondary circuit superimposed on the primary circuit. One end of the winding is in contact with the centre of a rotating arm, or distributor, that leads to the centre electrodes of a sparking plug. The other end of the secondary winding is connected via the primary winding to the earth electrode of the sparking plugs.

4.9 Magneto Operation.

Assuming that a current is flowing in the primary circuit when the contact breaker points are closed, then a magnetic field is also present around the primary and secondary windings, the strength of the field being dependent upon the strength of the current flow. If the cam is now operated, the contact points open, the primary circuit is broken, and primary current ceases to flow. This produces an immediate collapse of the magnetic field causing the lines of force to move across the secondary winding. Since any movement of lines of force across a conductor induces a voltage into that conductor a current will flow in the secondary circuit for the time taken for the field to collapse.

The current set up in the secondary circuit is fed to the distributor, the rotor of which is so timed that it is then opposite the segment leading to the sparking plug in the cylinder positioned for firing.

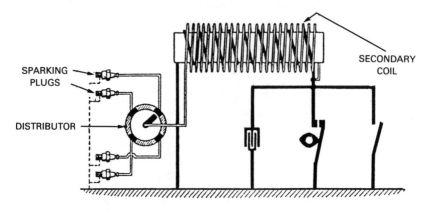

Fig.4-6. Complete Circuit with Secondary Coil Superimposed on Primary Circuit.

4.10 Distribution.

On a four stroke engine the cylinders need to be fired once in every two revolutions of the engine in a sequence (the firing order) that produces the least vibration. To do this high tension leads from the cylinder sparking plugs are connected in the sequence desired to segments spaced equally around the distributor block, and the distributor rotor is engine driven at half engine speed. Thus, the rotor passes each engine segment once in every two engine revolutions coupling individual cylinders to the secondary circuit in the same sequence as the firing order. (No matter how many cylinders there are on an engine the distributor rotor always rotates at half engine speed.) Therefore, provided a voltage is induced in the secondary winding whenever the rotor is opposite a segment, the secondary circuit is completed through the correct cylinder sparking plug.

Before such a voltage can be induced in the secondary windings a current must be flowing in the primary circuit; this is now considered. There are two basic methods of producing current in the primary circuit of a magneto, by rotating an armature within a magnetic field, or by rotating magnetic 'poles' to vary the field acting on a stationary armature (polar inductor).

Examples of each type are described in the following paragraphs.

4.11 Rotating Armature Magneto.

The armature of a rotating armature magneto is carried on an engine driven shaft that rotates between the poles of a permanent magnet. Fig.4-7 displays a diagrammatic representation of such an arrangement showing the flux, or lines of force changes, through the armature core during half a revolution of the shaft.

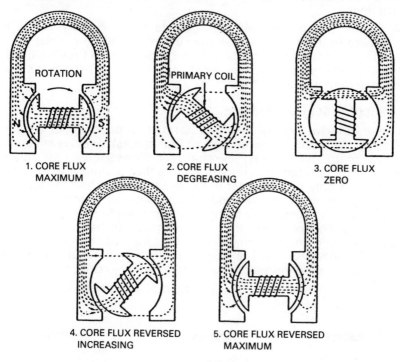

1. CORE FLUX MAXIMUM

2. CORE FLUX DEGREASING

3. CORE FLUX ZERO

4. CORE FLUX REVERSED INCREASING

5. CORE FLUX REVERSED MAXIMUM

Fig.4-7. Rotating Armature Magneto.

This change of flux causes a voltage to be induced into the primary winding and primary current results. The strength of this current will be at its peak in position 3, core flux zero, when the greatest change of magnetism on the armature occurs. It is at this point that the contact breaker points are made to open, i.e. when the magnetic field created by the primary current flow will also be at its maximum. Note that this zero core flux position occurs twice only in one revolution of the armature and consequently this type of magneto supplies two sparks/revs.

The contact breaker on this type of magneto is fixed to the armature shaft, the operating cam being held in the end casing. Thus, as the armature assumes position 3, and the primary current is at its maximum, the contact breaker points are automatically opened by the cams.

The current resulting from the induced voltage in the secondary circuit is fed from the rotating armature via a carbon brush and slip ring to the centre of the distributor rotor and thence, through the distributor segments to the sparking plugs.

This type of magneto is suitable only for light aircraft with a small number of cylinders because:

(a) Since two sparks only are supplied during each revolution the magneto speed becomes too high for engines of more than about six cylinders.

(b) Centrifugal force acting on the armature windings tend to burst the windings.

(c) A greater number of rubbing contacts are necessary inside the magneto in this type because the current has to be passed from a rotating to a stationary contact. Though the carbon brushes used at these points have a low resistance, a fixed contact is always more reliable than a rubbing contact.

4.12   Rotating Magnet Magneto.

This polar inductor type of magneto normally produces four electrical impulses in the secondary windings (or four sparks) for every revolution of the magneto shaft and is, therefore, far more suitable for engines having a large number of cylinders than is the rotating armature type magneto. Not only does a polar inductor type run at half the speed of the rotating armature type to produce the same number of sparks but the coils and switch assembly being stationary, are free from centrifugal loading. As a consequence, this type of magneto has largely super-seded the rotating armature magneto except for those engines with less than six cylinders, where the speed of the magneto at low engine speeds is too slow to generate an effective primary current.

Fig.4-8 shows an example of the principle of operation of an inductor type magneto.

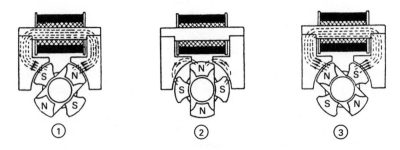

Fig.4-8. Rotating Magnet Magneto.

One form of polar inductor magneto is the rotating magnet type. The main rotating member of this type consists of a non-magnetic steel shaft on which is mounted a tubular magnet clamped between two, two fingered soft iron magnet pole pieces set 90 degrees apart. One end of the tube has a north polarity, the other end is of south polarity and the respective polarity is imparted to the clamping pole pieces. The assembly is rotated in a tunnel formed between the iron extensions of an armature core. This arrangement is shown diagrammatically, the three positions covering a quarter revolution of the shaft in Fig.4-8.

Flux changes through the armature core as the magnetic poles revolve produce a change of magnetism around the primary winding of the armature and the current resulting from the voltage thus induced in the primary winding reaches a maximum with the poles at position 2 (core flux zero). It is at this point that the contact breaker points are opened.

The stationary contact breaker assembly is normally housed at the non-driving end of the magneto so that a four lobed cam keyed to the end of the rotating shaft automatically opens the points when the primary current is at its peak. This arrangement does not apply to radial engines, where, the operating cam and contact breaker are contained within the distributor housing.

Fig.4-9 shows an exploded view of a rotating magnet magneto.

Although the primary current is produced in a somewhat different manner to the rotating armature type the secondary current is set up by an induced voltage in precisely the same way. Thus, when the contact breaker points interrupt the primary current, causing the primary magnetic field to collapse, a voltage is induced in the secondary circuit for the period of time that the lines of force cut across the secondary winding. Similarly, the voltage of the impulse so induced is dependent upon:

(a) The strength of the magnetic field created by the primary current. This again depends upon the strength of the permanent magnet, the speed of the magneto shaft, and the number of turns in the primary winding.

(b) The speed of movement of the collapsing lines of force. This is related to the time taken for the current flow to stop after the contact breaker points have begun to open. The current does not stop instantly; as the points open, current continues to flow, though at a falling rate, until the resistance of the air at the gap at the points becomes too high. In practice this lag in current shut-off is considerably reduced by the action of the condenser.

(c) The ratio between the number of turns in the secondary windings to the number of turns in the primary winding. The greater the ratio the greater is the relative step-up in the voltage of the secondary circuit to that in the primary.

The average voltage in the primary circuit of a magneto running at normal rpm is in the region of 27 volts; that of the secondary circuit is between 5000 and 7000 volts.

On engines where it is considered that the speed of a four pole inductor would be too high more than four poles are formed on the magneto shaft. Where this is so, more flux reversals occur per revolution of the magneto shaft and given a suitable contact breaker, more than four sparks/revs are produced. Alternatively, two separate armatures and contact breaker assemblies may be arranged in the tunnel.

4.13 Internal Timing.

To obtain the maximum electrical output from a magneto, it is essential

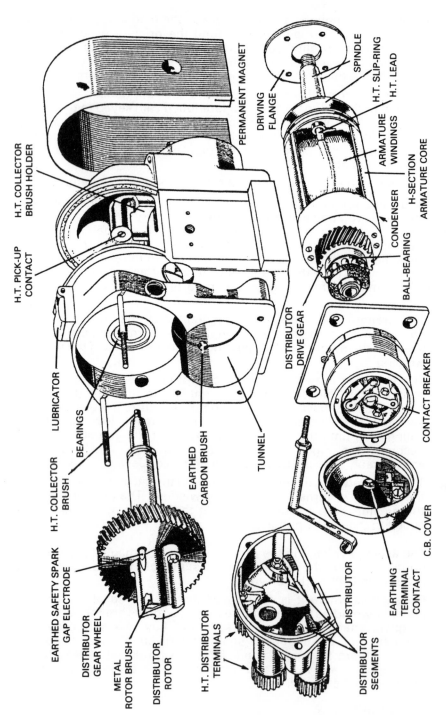

PERMANENT MAGNET

DRIVING FLANGE

SPINDLE

H.T. SLIP-RING

H.T. LEAD

ARMATURE WINDINGS

H-SECTION ARMATURE CORE

CONDENSER

BALL-BEARING

H.T. COLLECTOR BRUSH HOLDER

H.T. PICK-UP CONTACT

DISTRIBUTOR DRIVE GEAR

CONTACT BREAKER

C.B. COVER

EARTHING TERMINAL CONTACT

LUBRICATOR

BEARINGS

H.T. COLLECTOR BRUSH

EARTHED CARBON BRUSH

TUNNEL

EARTHED SAFETY SPARK GAP ELECTRODE

METAL ROTOR BRUSH

DISTRIBUTOR GEAR WHEEL

DISTRIBUTOR ROTOR

H.T. DISTRIBUTOR TERMINALS

DISTRIBUTOR SEGMENTS

DISTRIBUTOR

Fig.4-9. Construction of a Rotating Armature Magneto.

that the contact breaker points are opened when the primary current flow is at its peak. Further, to be sure the resulting secondary current flows to a cylinder spark plug, the distributor rotor must then be opposite a distributor segment. Normally, correct relative positioning (or internal timing) of the magnetic pole pieces, the contact breaker cam, and the distributor rotor is done during magneto assembly. In service however, wear on the contact breaker points and cam affect the relative positioning of these components and some adjustment may be necessary to maintain full efficiency.

4.14 Magneto Speed Ratios.

Every cylinder of an engine that works on the four stroke cycle require one spark every two revolutions of the engine crank shaft. Consequently, the greater the number of engine cylinders the faster the magneto needs to be driven to provide the necessary number of sparks.

In general, the speed of the magneto relative to the engine speed may be calculated as follows:

$$\text{Magneto Speed} = \frac{\text{Number of engine cylinders}}{2 \times \text{the number of sparks/revs}}$$

Thus, for a twelve cylinder engine fitted with a rotating magnet type magneto (4 sparks/revs) the magneto needs to be driven at

$$\frac{12}{2 \times 4} = 1\tfrac{1}{2} \text{ times the engine speed.}$$

Each segment of a distributor is connected to a different cylinder and each requires one spark every two engine revolutions. Therefore as explained before, the distributor rotor, irrespective of the magneto shaft speed, always rotates at half engine crankshaft speed.

4.15 Dual Ignition.

All aero-engines are fitted with dual ignition, i.e. two entirely independent ignition systems. Thus each cylinder has two sparking plugs, each fed from a different magneto. This is done to:

(a) Reduce the possibility of engine failure because of an ignition fault.

(b) Increase the engine power output. Power output can be increased on large bore cylinders by igniting the charge at two widely spaced points: this reduces the overall time taken to burn the full charge and so enables peak gas pressure to be reached before the piston has moved very far down its stroke.

4.16 Contact Breaker.

Though contact breaker assemblies vary widely in detail design the same basic action is always retained. A typical rotating magnet type contact breaker assembly is shown in Fig.4-10.

The assembly consists of a rocker arm that oscillates on a pivot pin secured to the base plate. One end of the rocker arm is fitted with a fibre 'heel' that contacts a four lobed cam, which is fitted to the magneto shaft. A movable contact point is mounted at the other end of the rocker, a 'fixed' point being secured to the base plate. A leaf spring attached to the rocker arm tends to hold the contacts together.

The cam is keyed to such a position on the magneto shaft that when it strikes the fibre heel of the rocker arm thus opening the points, the primary current flow is at its maximum. The contact breaker spring closes the points when the cam has passed the fibre heel. This cycle occurs four times every revolution of the magneto shaft and consequently both the mechanical and electrical stresses on the assembly are extensive.

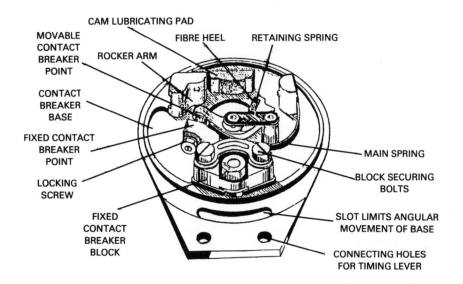

Fig.4-10. Contact Breaker Assembly.

4.17 Magneto Couplings and Ignition Timing.

In general to obtain the best possible engine performance the magnetos must be accurately timed to the engine. To be able to do this some form of magneto drive that provides an angular adjustment between the engine and the magneto is necessary. Many such magneto drive couplings are in use, some employing a vernier principle to provide a fine adjustment, others using fine pitched serrations or teeth.

4.18 Vernier Type Coupling.

The vernier coupling consists of three discs, the magneto drive, the so called flexible disc, and the magneto coupling. In the type illustrated, in Fig.4-11, the magneto drive, which is driven by the engine, has nineteen teeth, the magneto coupling, which is keyed to the magneto shaft, has twenty teeth. The intermediate flexible disc has nineteen on one side and twenty teeth on the other.

Referring to Fig.4-11 it can be seen that the difference in angular movement between one tooth on the magneto drive and one tooth on the magneto coupling = A. But one tooth on the magneto drive = 1/19 part of a revolution, and one tooth on the magneto coupling = 1/20 part of a revolution.

Therefore, A = 1/19 −1/20 = 20/380 − 19/380 = 1/380 rev = .95 degrees.

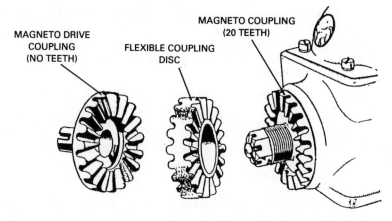

MAGNETO DRIVE COUPLING (NO TEETH)

FLEXIBLE COUPLING DISC

MAGNETO COUPLING (20 TEETH)

Fig.4-11. Vernier Type Magneto Coupling.

Thus, if the intermediate flexible disc is disengaged from the outer members and re-engaged in the next tooth in the same direction of rotation on each side the engine and magneto is altered by .95 degrees or approximately 1 degree. Whether this movement advances or retards the magneto depends on the direction of rotation taken by the flexible disc when making the fine adjustment.

4.19   Variable Ignition Timing.

The peak gas pressure generated within a cylinder should occur just after TDC when the piston is at the start of the power stroke. If peak pressure is reached before this point very little torque is produced and exceptionally heavy loads are placed on the crankshaft bearings because of the acute angle of the crankweb. If peak pressure is reached after this point not only has gas pressure been lost because of the increased volume above the piston but the actual working stroke has been shortened.

To ensure peak pressure always occurs at the same crankshaft position the following factors must be considered:

(a) Engine Speed.
     The faster an engine runs the greater is the arc of crankpin travel during the time taken for the charge to burn. Therefore, with an increase in engine speed the timing needs to be progressively advanced, with a reduction in engine speed the ignition timing should be retarded.

(b) Manifold Pressure.
     The greater the pressure of a gas the faster does it burn. Thus the cylinder charge of an engine running at high manifold pressure

burns quicker than a charge at low manifold pressure. Therefore, to stop the peak pressure position moving as manifold pressure is increased the ignition timing should be progressively retarded.

(a) Mixture Strength.
A correct mixture burns faster than either a 'weak' or 'rich' mixture. Therefore, any variation from a correct mixture strength demands a retardation of ignition timing.

There is a tendency for these factors to cancel out, e.g. high engine speed generally means high manifold pressure and rich mixture, but the cancellation is not exact.

On low powered engines the gain to be had from making slight adjustments to the ignition timing during engine running is usually too small to be considered. On the larger engines however, where the gain can be appreciable, ignition timing may be varied to suit all three conditions. Timing variation may be made either by a flexible coupling or by a variable drive.

4.20 Ignition Cable.

The high tension leads that connect the magneto and the high energy ignition units to the plugs are made of single cored, heavily insulated cable capable of carrying high voltages and of withstanding the ill effects of oil and fuel contamination and the engine high temperatures. The single core is made of twisted strands of either tinned copper or stainless steel and rubberised insulation. The insulation is generally protected by an outer covering of varnished fabric. Low tension cable used for wiring the switch into the magneto circuit is of similar construction but not quite so robust.

4.21 Ignition Harness.

On multi-cylinder engines it is usual to enclose the HT leads, as far as possible, in a metal conduit, or 'harness'. This has the advantages of:

(a) Positive screening with less weight.

(b) Protecting the leads from damage.

(c) Sealing the leads against moisture.

In practice, an ignition harness consists of one or more rigid conduits to which are attached two large diameter flexible conduits leading to the magneto distributors, and a number of smaller flexible conduits connecting to individual sparking plugs. The complete assembly is secured to the engine by attachment lugs on the rigid conduit. Each HT lead passes from the magneto distributor block through a large bore flexible conduit, and around the inside of the rigid conduit to the small flexible conduit leading to its spark plug. Each lead has a suitable identification sleeve at each end.

4.22 Screening.

The sudden variations in current flow and the arcing that takes place in the HT windings, leads, distributors and sparking plugs during normal operation produces unwanted signals that, unless suppressed, interfere with aircraft radio reception. Radiation of such signals is prevented by enclosing all the components of the ignition system in a non-magnetic metal screen.

The magnetos are screened by the body of the magneto and the fitting of cover plates over the contact breaker and distributor block. HT leads are screened either by enclosing them in metal conduit (ignition harness) or by the use of braided cables. Screening is effective in eliminating any such interference only where all screening is electrically connected, or 'bonded', to the airframe structure.

4.23 Bonding.

All metal parts of an aircraft must be in good electrical contact one to another so that all have the same electrical charge, or potential. Unless this is done any intermittent contact that causes arcing between parts or components at different potentials produce radio interference and also increases the danger of fire. In practice pipelines, metal braided leads, metal conduit and other components that are not in constant metallic contact with the airframe are all bonded to the airframe structure with special clips or wires.

4.24 Sparking Plugs General.

Sparking plugs are the means whereby the electrical energy generated by the magneto is used to ignite the mixture in the cylinder. The plug has two electrodes which are positioned to form a gap across which the HT current creates a spark.

An aero-engine sparking plug consists of three main parts, viz:

(a) A hollow steel body, which screws into the cylinder; the lower end of the body carries the earth electrodes.

(b) A centre assembly, comprising the central electrode and its insulation. A metal washer is fitted between the central electrode and the body to make the joint gas-tight.

(c) A hollow steel gland nut which secures the centre assembly to the body.

The sparking plug is subjected to intense heat, highly corrosive gases and a high electrical voltage. Sparking plugs are designed for use in particular makes, types and marks of aero-engine and it is essential that only approved plug types for that particular engine are used.

Fig.4-12 shows an example of a screened sparking plug.

4.25 Auxiliary Ignition Devices for Engine Starting.

When starting a piston type aero-engine it is seldom that the engine is turned over fast enough for the magnetos to operate and some other means of providing the essential spark becomes necessary. In general, the method used is decided by the size of the engine and aircraft. Low powered engines use impulse starters and larger aircraft or engines use some form of booster coil. Both methods are described below.

(a) Impulse Starter.
   The impulse starter is used on low powered engines and on light aircraft where the aircraft is started by hand swinging the propeller.

The unit is a spring loaded coupling through which the engine drives one of the magnetos. The drive passes from the engine half of the coupling through a strong spiral spring to the magneto half of the coupling.

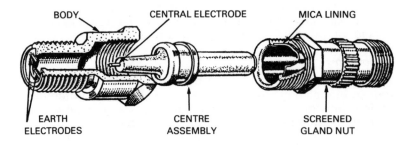

BODY CENTRAL ELECTRODE MICA LINING

EARTH ELECTRODES CENTRE ASSEMBLY SCREENED GLAND NUT

Fig.4-12. Screened Sparking Plug.

Operation.
When turning the engine to start, the magneto turns with the engine until just before the magneto contact breaker points are about to open. At this point the pawl falls against a stop on the magneto end plate and prevents further magneto rotation. Continued engine turning winds up the spiral spring until, just after TDC, a cam on the engine coupling releases the pawl. The spring then unwinds rapidly and flicks the magneto round fast enough to produce a spark, which is so far retarded that there is no danger of a 'kick back' of the propeller. The pawls are so mass balanced that centrifugal force holds them out of engagement during normal engine running.

4.26 High Tension Booster Coil.

High tension booster coils are used for engine starting where an electric battery is available. The unit supplies a continual stream of high tension electrical impulses each capable of producing a spark at the sparking plug. These impulses are directed to the cylinders in the correct firing order through an additional 'trailing' brush on the engine magneto distributor rotor.

The HT booster coil consists of an armature and an electrically operated switch. The armature, as in the magneto, has a soft iron core on which is wound primary and secondary windings. The electrically operated switch controls the primary circuit and the movable contact of the switch is secured to a leaf spring, which tends to hold the contacts closed. The hook of a flexible steel plate, upon which is mounted a soft iron pad, is caught under the leaf spring.

Operation.
When a current is fed into the primary circuit from external batteries a magnetic field is built up around the armature and the core becomes magnetised. The magnetised core immediately attracts the iron pad causing the hook to open the contact points and break the primary circuits.

This causes:

(a) The magnetic field to collapse across the secondary winding and so induce a high tension electrical impulse that is fed to the trailing brush of the magneto distributor rotor of the engine.

(a) The armature to lose its magnetism thus allowing the leaf spring to close the contact points.

The moment the contact points close the primary circuit is again energised and the cycle is repeated and continues to be repeated until the battery is switched off. Thus an endless stream of high tension impulses is fed to the distributor of the main magneto and on to its sparking plug.

As on a magneto, a condenser is fitted across the contact points to reduce arcing at the points and increase the speed of collapse of the primary current and magnetic field.

4.27   Low Tension Booster Coil.

This type of booster coil is used where the normal timing of the engine is retarded sufficiently for starting purposes. The operation of the unit is basically the same as the HT booster coil but a separate starter brush on the magneto distributor rotor is not required. This removes any chance of flash over at altitude and consequent engine misfiring.

TEST YOURSELF 4
PISTON ENGINE IGNITION

1. The magnetic field in a magneto is provided by:
   (a) battery current.
   (b) an excitation field circuit.
   (c) a permanent magnet.
   Ref. 4.8.

2. Excessive arcing across the contact breaker points of a magneto when the points are open is prevented by:
   (a) a diode being fitted.
   (b) a condenser being fitted.
   (c) insulation of the contacts.
   Ref. 4.8.

3. If the switch of a magneto becomes disconnected in flight:
   (a) the affected magneto will automatically be isolated.
   (b) the alternative magneto will maintain ignition.
   (c) the affected magneto will continue to provide a spark.
   Ref. 4.8.

4. On a four stroke engine the ignition spark will occur:
   (a) once each revolution of the engine.
   (b) once very fourth revolution of the engine.
   (c) once every two revolutions of the engine.
   Ref. 4.10.

5. On engine start up, the generator warning light fails to extinguish, this will result in:
   (a) the engine stopping when the battery is totally discharged.
   (b) failure of the initial excitation of the magneto.
   (c) the engine continuing to run normally.
   Ref. 4.7.

6. The primary coil of a magneto consists of:
   (a) fewer windings of thicker wire than the secondary coil.
   (b) fewer windings of thin wire than the secondary coil.
   (c) fewer windings of the same thickness of wire as the secondary coil.
   Ref. 4.8.

7. The distributor rotor on a four stroke engine rotates at:
   (a) the same speed as the engine.
   (b) twice the speed of the engine.
   (c) half the speed of the engine.

   Ref. 4.10.

8. With increase of engine speed, ignition timing:
   (a) will advance.
   (b) will retard.
   (c) will remain constant.

   Ref. 4.19.

9. A Booster Coil provides:
   (a) a continuous stream of high tension electrical impulses.
   (b) a pulsed stream of low tension electricity.
   (c) a continuous stream of low tension electrical impulses.

   Ref. 4.26.

10. To assist with engine starting, some engine ignition system sparks may be:
    (a) advanced.
    (b) pulsed.
    (c) retarded

    Ref. 4.27.

5

FUEL SYSTEMS

5.1 Introduction.

The aircraft fuel system consists primarily of the fuel tank in which the fuel is stored during flight, fuel pumps to supply the engine, or engines, with fuel when it is required, and filters to ensure the fuel is clean for use in the engine systems. Some engine fuel systems may be fitted with on/off cocks for the purpose of isolating the fuel system or sections of it, when it is not in use.

5.2 Fuel Tanks.

Aircraft fuel tanks are normally located in the wings or fuselage of civil aircraft, in some instances additional fuel tanks have been located in such places as fins, flaps and external auxiliary tanks to increase the aircraft's total fuel storage capacity.

Fuel tanks may be or rigid, flexible of integral construction and are connected by pipelines in such a way that on larger aircraft fuel may be transferred from one tank to another whilst in flight. If such systems are fitted in the event of engine failure on a multi-engined aircraft, fuel may be transferred from one wing or location to the other to maintain supply of fuel to the other engine or engines. Transfer of fuel in this way is achieved by operation of controls in the cockpit, which usually take the form of switches, to control on/off cocks and transfer pumps. Fig.5-1 shows the layout of a simple fuel system.

5.3 Fuel Pumps.

Engine driven fuel pumps normally associated with the fuel systems of piton engined aircraft may be classified as follows:

(a) Gear type pumps.

(b) Rotary vane type pumps.

(c) Diaphragm type pumps.

5.4 Gear Type Pumps.

These are similar in operation to engine oil pumps, but are not regarded as being totally satisfactory when handling high octane fuels, particularly at the high altitudes required by some modern aircraft. Positive delivery pumps of this and rotary vane types are usually provided with a diaphragm operated relief valve which maintains a constant delivery pressure irrespective of pump suction conditions. Fuel serving this pump acts also as a lubricant; because of this the pump should never be allowed to run dry.

See Fig.5-2.

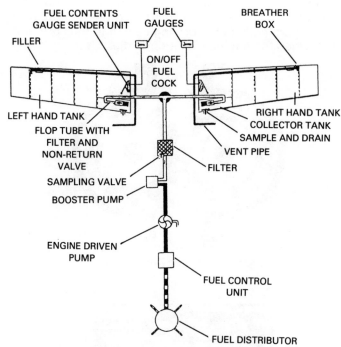

Fig.5-1. Simple Fuel System.

5.5 Rotary Vane Type Pumps.

In this type of pump, a number of flat vanes are arranged radially in a central rotor which is situated eccentrically within the pump casing. As the rotor moves round, the space between the vanes increase and decrease, the rotor blades sliding in and out of the slots and being kept in contact with the wall of the casing by centrifugal force. The inlet port allows fuel to enter the chamber as its volume is increasing, while the outlet allows fuel which has passed through the pump to be forced out as the crescent shaped space is decreasing. A relief valve by-passes the excess fuel as a result of excess pressure from the delivery side to the inlet side. Since the fuel acts as a lubricant to the vanes, this pump should not be run in a dry condition.

Fig.5-3 shows an example of a rotary vane type pump.

5.6 Diaphragm Type Pumps.

Fuel pumps of this category operate on the principle of a reciprocating diaphragm working within a closed chamber provided with spring loaded inlet and outlet valves. This pump is usually engine driven, the reciprocating (backwards and forwards) motion of the diaphragm being derived from a rotating cam operating direct on to a plunger connected to the centre of the diaphragm, as shown in Fig.5-4. When cam operated, the plunger and diaphragm are pressed outwards by a spring which keeps the plunger pad in continuous contact with the contour of the cam. Sometimes the diaphragm plunger is spring loaded internally to regulate the maximum pressure of fuel which can be delivered by the pump. A separate lever is usually provided to operate the plunger and diaphragm independently of the driving cam, and thus prime the pump and fuel lines when the engine is standing idle.

Fig.5-2 Spur Gear Type Pump.

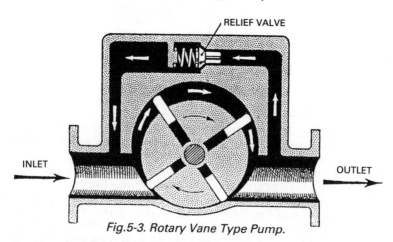

Fig.5-3. Rotary Vane Type Pump.

5.7 Booster Pumps, Transfer Pumps and Transfer Systems.

(a) Booster pumps.

Booster pumps are electrically operated. They may be fitted externally in the pipe leading from the tank or a group of tanks, or may be of the immersed type fitted within the tank at its outlet. When the booster pump is not switched on, a by-pass permits fuel to flow from the tank under suction from the engine driven pump.

The purpose of the booster pump is:

(i) To prevent any portion of the fuel system from falling below atmospheric pressure and by this means, prevent vapour locks forming in the pipes.

(ii)   To supply adequate fuel to the engine driven pumps during take-off, landing, at high engine settings and high altitude.

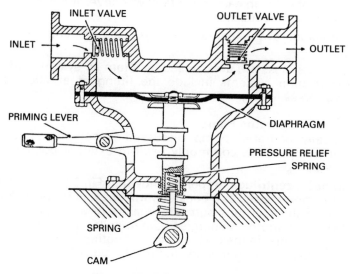

Fig.5-4 Diaphragm Type Pump

(b) Warning Indication and Control.

In many aircraft, a fuel pressure warning light is fitted to the instrument panel to serve each engine. This lights up when the pressure at the carburettor or injector falls below a pre-determined minimum. In some systems, warning lights are fitted to the circuits of each booster and transfer pump. These lights come on when the pumps are not switched on, or are functioning incorrectly.

Booster pumps should be switched on if the fuel pressure warning light comes on or flickers when the engine is running. They should never be left on after an engine has been stopped or when the fuel tanks concerned are empty.

(c) Transfer Pumps.

The same type of pump, when fitted in a tank or system which does not feed an engine direct, is known as a fuel transfer pump, and serves to pump fuel from this tank into another tank or collector box which feeds the engine direct.

Note: A collector box or collector tank is an assembly into which fuel is fed or directed prior to being collected by the suction of the engine driven pump.

5.8   Fuel Tank Pressurisation.

Some aircraft fuel tanks, in particular auxiliary tanks, are pressurised to force fuel from them to the engine or main tanks. Fuel tanks are pressurised in a number of ways, one such example is that pressure is fed from the exhaust side of the vacuum pumps, which is then fed to the fuel tank venting system which is then sealed.

When auxiliary fuel tanks are used to replenish main tanks they are pressurised at all times, fuel being transferred automatically under control of a float valve in each main tank whenever the contents of the latter fall below a predetermined level.

The pressurisation of the fuel tank or tanks also prevents cavitation at the pumps.

Note: Some fuel tanks are pressurised by a ram air system and all fuel tank pressurisation systems include the fitting of a relief valve to prevent over pressurising.

5.9 Electrically Operated Pumps.

The electrically operated pump discussed is sometimes termed a pulsometer pump and is commonly used in external booster pumps and transfer pumps.

The pump has a centrifugal impeller, shown in Fig.5-5 which is driven by an electric motor. Used as a booster pump the unit is normally bolted to the base of the fuel tank sump by means of a flanged mounting bracket. When the motor is energised the impeller draws fuel from the tank through the inlet in the centre of the mounting flange and delivers it through the discharge connection to the inlet side of the engine driven pump.

Note: In the event of pump failure fuel can still be drawn through the pump by the engine driven pump.

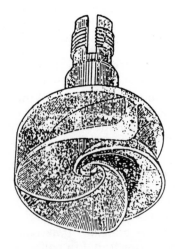

Fig.5-5 Impeller of Pulsometer Pump.

5.10 Hand Operated Priming Pumps.

An example of a hand operated priming pump is shown in Fig.5-6. This type of pump is generally used on light aircraft for starting engines.

Hand operated it delivers fuel to the induction manifold jets, and is sometimes used to fill the carburettor float chamber initially through a three-way cock.

When the plunger is pushed right in, it may be locked by screwing tight, thus, pressing a tufnol pad against the lower end of the cylinder. This blocks the inlet and outlet ports and ensures that no fuel can be drawn through the pump by induction when the engine is running. The inlet and outlet ports are fitted with spring loaded non-return ball valves. A gland, gland nut and locking nut prevent leaks around the plunger.

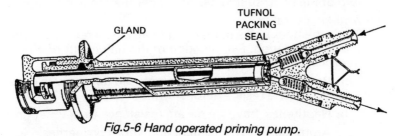

Fig.5-6 Hand operated priming pump.

Failure to depress the plunger and lock it on completion of priming will result in fuel being drawn through the pump direct into the inlet manifold by the suction of the engine's pistons by-passing the carburettor resulting in a rich mixture or possibly flooding the engine.

5.11 Electrically Operated Priming Pumps.

Piston engined aircraft fitted with fuel injection systems are normally primed by operation of an electrically operated pump, usually in the form of a booster type. It should be noted the booster pump, on starting, is only used to prime the engine fuel system and is then switched off before any attempt is made to start the engine. If the booster pump should be left on during starting this could, in some cases, result in flooding the engine.

Note: Priming the engine fuel system is to fill the system with fuel and not to pressurise it.

5.12 Aviation Gasoline Fuels.

(a) Properties.

Gasolines, suitable for use in piston engines designed for aircraft, have high anti-knock ratings, low freezing point, high overall volatility and high stability. These together with the solvent and corrosion properties are briefly discussed below.

(i) Anti-Knock Rating.

To appreciate the need for a fuel of high anti-knock rating, the cause of detonation must be understood. Vapourised fuel mixed with air within a certain range of proportions (fuel/air ratio) forms a combustible mixture and when ignited generates heat. Providing that the combustion rate is steady, the heat generated can be efficiently converted into mechanical energy until all the charge is burnt. If a charge of mixture is ignited in a confined space (combustion chamber), the decreasing unburned portion of charge will be steadily heated by radiation, and compression due to the increase in pressure, of the burnt portion. The temperature of the unburned portion may be raised so high that it ignites spontaneously and combustion is completed in the form of an explosion. Such a condition is known as "Detonation" and, when occurring in an aircraft engine, causes serious loss of power, excessive temperature and eventual mechanical failure. Incorrect mixture strength and use of a fuel with a poor anti-knock value are two of the contributing causes of detonation in an engine.

(ii) Anti-knock Value.
The anti-knock value of fuel is defined as the resistance the fuel has to detonation. Examination of the behaviour of a range of hydrocarbon fuels in an engine shows that:

    a. Paraffins (Heptane, has pronounced tendency to detonate. Iso-octane resists detonation).

    b. Napthenes, have moderate resistance to detonation.

    c. Aromatics, have excellent anti-knock properties.

Thus the anti-knock value of a fuel is dependent on the portions of its hydrocarbon contents. By selective blending fuels of high anti-knock ratings are produced. By research, it has also been established that the anti-knock value of a fuel varies with the fuel/air ratio, the value being lower for a weak mixture and higher for a rich mixture.

Apart from the choice of hydrocarbons, the anti-knock rating of gasoline is effectively increased by the addition of metallic compounds. Tetra-ethyl lead, a chemical compound of a hydrocarbon with lead, is the most powerful and best known anti-knock compound in use.

(iii) Volatility.
The definition of a volatile liquid is one which is capable of readily changing from the liquid to the vapour state by the application of heat, or by contact with a gas into which it can evaporate. The mixture of hydrocarbon components of a gasoline, boil at different temperatures, the lowest components boiling at about 100F and the highest at about 340F.

(iv) Solvent Properties.
Aromatic hydrocarbons, forming up to 20 per cent, by volume of high grade aviation gasoline, are powerful solvents of ruber and some rubber like compounds. It is therefore essential that care is exercised, during handling and filling operations, to ensure that gasoline is not spilled on aircraft tyres and other rubber covered components.

(v) Corrosive Properties.
The corrosive effects of gasoline are caused by the sulphur and additive contents. Gasoline will have corrosive effects to components it comes into contact with in both its burnt and unburnt state. New alloys and treatments to surfaces has helped to reduce the corrosive effects.

Note: The most common fuel used for piston engined aircraft is 100 LL, which is dyed blue.

TEST YOURSELF 5
FUEL SYSTEMS

1. Fuel pumps:
   (a) should not be run when the fuel system is dry.
   (b) of all types are lubricated by the fuel that passes through them.
   (c) are normally electrically operated.

   Ref. 5.4.

2. Booster pumps are:
   (a) normally driven by the engine.
   (b) electrically operated.
   (c) normally used for priming the engine only.

   Ref. 5.7.

3. If the fuel pressure warning light comes on in flight the:
   (a) booster pumps must be isolated.
   (b) main fuel pump must be isolated.
   (c) booster pumps must be switched on.

   Ref. 5.7.

4. In the event of booster pump failure, the:
   (a) fuel will continue to be drawn through the booster pump by-pass by the engine driven pump.
   (b) pump must be isolated and the remaining fuel in the tank transferred by the transfer pumps.
   (c) fuel will be isolated in the tank.

   Ref. 5.9.

5. Fuel pump delivery is normally:
   (a) supplied at a constant flow rate to the engine.
   (b) supplied at a constant pressure, controlled by a pressure relief valve.
   (c) supplied at a constant volume.

   Ref. 5.4

6

COOLING SYSTEMS

6.1 Introduction.

Of the total heat produced by the burning of the fuel in the combustion chamber of a piston engine, about one-third is converted into useful energy and about two-fifths passes direct to the atmosphere with the exhaust gases. The remaining heat is absorbed by the pistons, cylinder heads, cylinders, etc, and by the lubricating oils which splash the cylinder walls and the underside of the pistons. Consequently, a cooling system becomes necessary to dissipate this heat so that the components can run at a safe working temperature. Unless the component temperature is controlled, distortion from expansion may cause seizure, or the strength of the material may drop to a degree where failure results. Excessive temperature may also cause the oil film to break down and can lead to the destruction of the lubricating properties of the oil. Conversely, to run an engine cold is to run it inefficiently, just as dissipating heat that can be turned into useful work is to waste energy. The transfer of the excess heat of the engine to the atmosphere may be either direct as with air cooling or by the use of a circulating liquid as with liquid cooled engines.

6.2 Air Cooling.

With air cooling all the surfaces that need to be cooled are usually extensively finned and a flow of air is directed over the exposed surfaces. The fins are kept thin and as close together as compatible with a free passage of air, thus securing a large cooling surface area in contact with the air. With fin areas that are out of the main air stream, deflectors may be used to redirect the air, or finning may be extended in that region, to maintain a uniform overall component temperature; uneven temperature will distort the engine components giving rise to a high rate of wear and a general loss in efficiency. Control of the direction of air flow is effected by fixed baffles and cowlings and by movable shutters or guides. It is essential that the baffles and cowlings are close fitting and are not distorted, or the disturbance from the designed flow will cause serious overheating. To maintain the efficiency of the system fins must be kept clean and free from dust or oil. A guide to the engine temperature is provided by a cylinder head temperature gauge.

6.3 Liquid Cooling.

With a liquid cooled engine the engine temperature is controlled by circulating a cooling fluid around the space between the jackets fitted

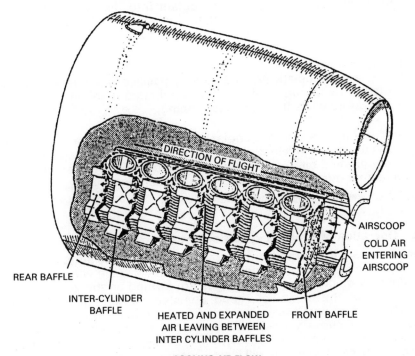

REAR BAFFLE

INTER-CYLINDER BAFFLE

DIRECTION OF FLIGHT

AIRSCOOP

COLD AIR ENTERING AIRSCOOP

HEATED AND EXPANDED AIR LEAVING BETWEEN INTER CYLINDER BAFFLES

FRONT BAFFLE

COOLING AIR FLOW

Fig.6-1. Air Cooled System.

round the cylinders and the cylinder walls, and through passages drilled in the cylinder head. The basic coolant is water, but because of the low temperatures found at altitude, the addition of an anti-freeze agent is essential; thus, the coolant used in an aero engine is a mixture of water and glycol. A simple system consists of the following:

(a) The Header Tank.
This tank, positioned at the top of the system, stores the reserve of coolant and provides a head of coolant to the pump.

(b) The Circulating Pump.
This is usually a centrifugal pump but does not produce pressure it is fitted to increase the speed of the coolant flow through the system and so reduce the quantity of coolant required.

(c) Operation.
The coolant passes through the engine. While the main passages are centred around the cylinder heads and valves, it is sometimes found that the hot coolant is directed to jackets fitted to the induction pipe and supercharger casings. This auxiliary flow assists in vapourising the fuel/air mixture. The cooland flow through the engine is arranged to follow the normal course of the thermal current, i.e. from the base of the cylinders to the cylinder head.

(d) The Radiator.
The radiator is normally positioned in the slipstream of the propeller

and dissipates the heat of the coolant into the air. Shutters are positioned at the rear of the radiator; when the coolant temperature falls below an efficient figure the shutters are inched closed, either automatically or manually.

(e) The Thermostat.
This is a thermostatically operated by-pass valve which effects the coolant flow through the radiator and limits the minimum coolant temperature while the engine is running.

Note: Cleanliness of both the coolant and the system is imperative if the system is to remain efficient; the radiator matrix must be kept clean and free from dirt and oil. A gauge, fitted in the cockpit, gives an indication of the temperature of the coolant in the header tank.

Fig.6-2 shows a simple liquid coolant system.

6.4   Operation of Typical Liquid Coolant System.

Coolant enters the pump from the radiator through the large inlet at the bottom. The pump is of the normal type with a sixteen vaned rotor and a volute. Two curved outlet passages are formed on the volute, one to each side of the engine. A hand adjusted packing gland prevents coolant leakage past the pump spindle, and lubrication is by a screw down grease cup. Excessive lubrication of the spindle will result in grease entering the coolant system and possibly becoming trapped in the cylinder head, where it will cause overheating. Extra lubrication will not cure a leaking gland. The pump is fitted with a drain cock at is lowest point for use when draining the system.

From the end of each outlet passage from the pump volute a curved pipe carries the coolant to a junction box on each of the cylinder blocks situated low down at the rear on the exhaust side. Inside the block the coolant passes round each cylinder liner, through the passages surrounding the combustion head and valve ports and thence to the outlets. A coolant manifold connects the cylinder liner jackets together on the exhaust side. There are three outlets, one at each end and one in the centre of the inlet side at the top of each block. These outlets are connected by a pipe on each block which carries the coolant towards the front of the engine. Each pipe is connected independently to the header tank, and from the header tank the coolant passes to the radiator. Each front cylinder block outlet elbow is fitted with an air vent plug to facilitate complete filling.

On the "A" side rear outlet elbow a connection is formed from which a pipe carries a small stream of hot coolant to a union on the carburettor heating jacket. The outlet from this jacket is on the starboard side and the coolant returns to the pump through a small auxiliary inlet branch on the main inlet.

Pipe junctions on the engine are made with a large circular nut round the pipe flange and a rubber gland to make the joint coolant-tight. Pipe junctions on the remainder of the coolant system are usually made with short lengths of reinforced rubber tubing or hose clipped to the pipe ends with circumferential clips.

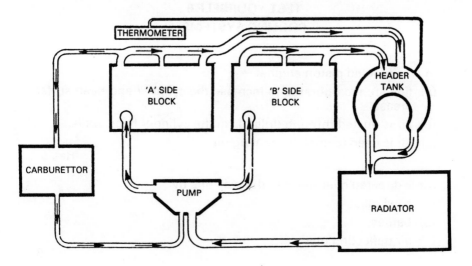

Fig.6-2. Liquid Cooled System.

1. In an aircooled piston engine:
   (a) fins are incorporated to increase the cylinder and head surface areas.
   (b) air is ducted through drillings in the cylinder head walls.
   (c) air is used to cool the cooling oil.

   Ref. 6.2.

2. Air is directed over the cylinder wall fins by:
   (a) cowl gills.
   (b) baffles.
   (c) air deflection plates.

   Ref. 6.2

3. Engine temperature is normally indicated by:
   (a) cylinder head temperature gauge.
   (b) the engine master temperature gauge.
   (c) the engine lubrication system temperature gauge.

   Ref. 6.2

4. Cooling air is normally provided by:
   (a) airflow from a supercharger.
   (b) airflow from a compressor bleed.
   (c) ram air.

   Ref. 6.2

5. In a liquid cooled engine cooling system:
   (a) temperature is controlled by a thermostat.
   (b) temperature is controlled by a master pump.
   (c) fuel is used to cool the coolant.

   Ref. 6.3

7

FLOAT CHAMBER CARBURETTORS AND FUEL INJECTIONS

7.1 Introduction.

Carburation is the process of supplying the correct amount of fuel for mixing and vapourising with the air induced into the engine to form a suitable combustible mixture. The proportions of fuel to air in a chemically correct or normal mixture is approximately 1 to 15 by weight. This mixture is theoretically the most efficient for all engine running conditions, but in practice it is sometimes necessary or advantageous to use either a 'rich' mixture (one with a higher proportion of fuel), or a 'weak' mixture (one with a higher proportion of air). The device employed for supplying the necessary amount of fuel to form the most suitable mixture for any engine running conditions may be either a float type carburettor or some form of fuel injection unit. This chapter describes both the working principle of the simple float type carburettor, and the modifications which are embodied to adapt it for efficient operation to suit piston aero-engine requirements.

7.2 The Simple Float Type Carburettor.

(a) Description.

In its simplest form the carburettor may consist of a tube or jet mounted in a larger tube in which is arranged a throttle valve and choke tube. In addition, the jet is connected to a float chamber, vented to atmosphere, which houses a float operating a needle valve. A pre-determined and constant level of fuel is maintained in the float chamber and the jet, by means of the float and needle mechanism.

(b) Operation.

Air drawn into the engine cylinder, governed by the degree of throttle opening, enters the carburettor through the air intake. At the restriction caused by the choke tube the velocity of the air is increased. The increased velocity of the air, within the choke tube and in the region of the jet, is accompanied by a fall in pressure below that of the atmosphere. As the fuel in the float chamber is subject to atmospheric pressure, a higher pressure than around the jet, fuel issues from the jet and mixes with the air stream flowing to the engine cylinders. The fall in the level of the fuel in the float chamber lowers the float which lifts the needle valve off its seating, permitting more fuel to flow into the float chamber to replace that issuing from the jet.

(c) Limitation.
Any increase in airflow will increase the pressure difference acting across the jet and consequently increase the fuel flow. The fuel flow, however, does not vary proportionately with greater air flow, and the mixture obtained from the simple carburettor becomes progressively richer as the engine speed is increased.

Fig.7-1 shows a simple carburettor.

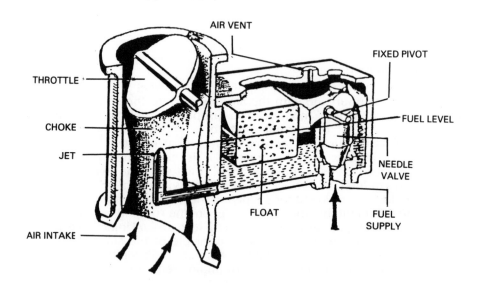

Fig.7-1. Simple Float Type Carburettor.

Note: From time to time alternative names are given to components fitted to aircraft, and the carburation system is no exception, therefore to assist in your understanding of the system as a whole alternative names are used in order to familiarise you with them. For example:

(a) Throttle .... often called the Butterfly
(b) Needle Valve .... sometimes termed the Float Valve
(c) Choke .... equally termed the venturi
(d) Air Vent .... often called the Breather

7.3 Modifications to a Simple Carburettor.

The following additions and modifications have been made to the simple carburettor, to provide one more suitable for use on piston type aero-engines.

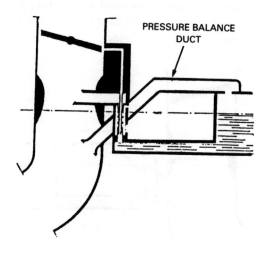

Fig.7-2. Pressure Balance Duct.

(a) Pressure Balance Air System.
   To prevent upsetting the rate of discharge of fuel from the jet, the atmospheric pressure in the air intake and in the float chamber must be equal. Admitting atmospheric pressure into the float chamber through a drilling in the float chamber cover is not a satisfactory method of ensuring equalised pressures on an aero-engine carburettor because due to manoeuvre and speed of the aircraft, the changes of pressure localised around the air intake would not be readily transmitted to the float chamber. Equalised pressure conditions, however are obtained by admitting atmospheric pressure to the float chamber, through a tube or duct opening into the air intake. This pressure balance duct also supplies air to the diffuser, and is used in some carburettors to provide altitude mixture control.

Fig.7-2 shows the position of the pressure balance duct.

(b) Diffuser.
   A diffuser is fitted to prevent the main jet supplying excessive fuel as the engine speed is increased; it ensures that the fuel flow is kept directly proportional to the volume of air flowing through the choke. The diffuser is basically a tube, drilled with a number of radial holes, and is positioned in the body of the carburettor above the main jet. The annular space between the diffuser and its housing is in communication with the pressure balance air system. Fuel enters the diffuser through the jet and when the engine is not running, the fuel level in the diffuser and the annular space is the same as that in the float chamber. During operation, as the engine speed is increased the fuel level in the annular space falls, thereby uncovering some of the radial holes. This allows air to flow through the holes into the diffuser, thus lessening the pressure difference acting across the jet and counteracting the tendency of the jet to supply

excessive fuel. The diffuser, in addition to fulfilling its primary function, also breaks down or emulsifies the fuel before the fuel is passed into the air stream flowing to the induction manifold.

Fig.7-3 shows the position of the diffuser.

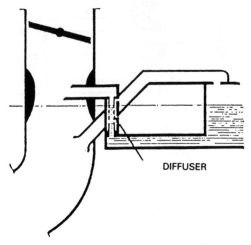

DIFFUSER

Fig.7-3. Diffuser.

(c) Slow Running Jet.

At small throttle openings the depression in the choke is practically negligible and no fuel flows from the main jet. A separate flow running jet is fitted, therefore, to supply the fuel necessary for slow running. The jet discharges near to the edge of the almost closed throttle, the strong depression at this point giving the necessary pressure difference. As the throttle is opened the depression at the throttle edge increases; the slow running jet will go out of action and the main jet will come into action. The slow running jet is arranged to give the rich mixture required over the idling range. Adjustment is usually carried out by an adjusting screw, movement of which has the effect of varying the pressure difference acting across the jet.

Fig.7-4 shows the slow running jet location.

(d) Power Jet.

The mixture strength supplied by the diffuser for 'cruising' condition is too weak for the engine to develop its full power output. To supply the extra fuel necessary to give the desired mixture strength for full power, the size or number of jets must be increased. Where a variable main jet is fitted its effective size is varied by the withdrawal of a tapered needle from the jet orifice; where a fixed main jet is fitted an additional jet is brought into action by the opening of a cam operated valve.

Fig.7-5 shows the power jet.

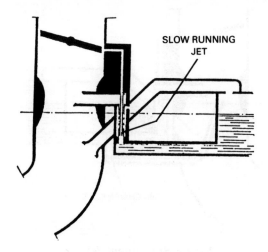

Fig.7-4. Slow Running Jet.

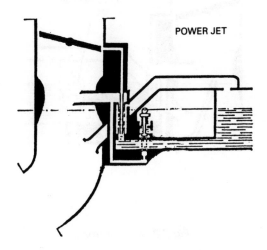

Fig.7-5. Power Jet.

(e) Enrichment Jet.
For the short period necessary at 'take-off' for an aircraft to become safely airborne, the maximum permissible engine power is required and supercharged engines are designed to develop additional power for this purpose. One method of obtaining this increase in power with safety is to supply the engine with a very rich mixture. The fuel for this purpose is delivered from an enrichment jet which operates in a similar manner to the cam-operated power jet.

Fig.7-6 indicates the position of the enrichment jet.

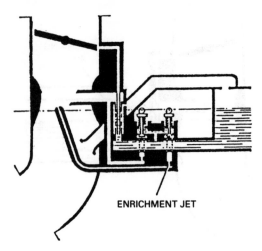

ENRICHMENT JET

Fig.7-6. Enrichment Jet.

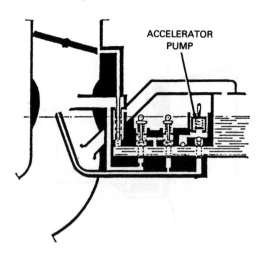

ACCELERATOR
PUMP

Fig.7-7. Accelerator.

(f) Accelerator Pump.

If the throttle is opened suddenly, the mixture supplied to the cylinders is momentarily too weak, partly because there is a lag in the increase of fuel flow from the jet, and because some of the fuel adheres to the walls of the induction system and does not reach the cylinders. An accelerator pump operated by the movement of the throttle lever, injects fuel into the airstream to make up for this temporary deficiency.

Sometimes a spring operated delayed action pump maintains the flow for a few seconds after the throttle opening has ceased.

Fig.7-7 shows the inclusion of the accelerator pump.

(g) Mixture Control.

The density of air decreases with increasing altitude and consequently less weight of air is induced for the same velocity of air through the choke. Thus a carburettor using the venturi choke as an airflow meter, delivers a progressively richer mixture as the altitude of operation increases.

Various methods are employed to correct the mixture strength at altitude. In the smaller aircraft engines this mixture control is hand operated, but on engines of medium and high power output, mixture strength is automatically controlled.

The methods employed for correcting mixture strength for altitude are as follows:

(i) Vacuum Control.

The pressure difference acting on the jet is reduced by connecting the float chamber to the choke via an orifice whose size is varied by the mixture control cock. By opening the cock the float chamber pressure can be reduced to give a pressure difference across the jet consistent with the mixture strength required.

Fig.7-8 shows the position of the mixture control.

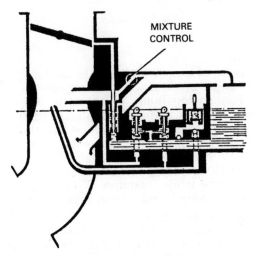

MIXTURE CONTROL

Fig.7-8. Mixture Control.

(ii) Diffuser Air Bleed.

Air is by-passed through the mixture control cock, from the pressure balance air system to the top of the diffuser thus reducing the pressure difference across the jet.

Note: A combination of (i) and (ii) is common in some types of carburettors.

(h) Cut Out Valve.

To stop a running engine, the ignition is switched off, but, due to the engine being hot and fuel being available at the slow running jet, the engine may continue running for a time, albeit erratically. To prevent this occurring a device is inserted into the slow running passage, which, when operated prevents any fuel from being drawn into the induction system.

Fig.7-9 shows the cut out valve position in a carburettor.

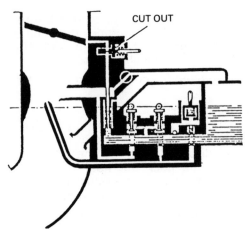

Fig.7-9. Cut Out.

(i) 'Anti-G' Devices.
When the direction of an aircraft is suddenly changed, forces which oppose the change of direction are imposed upon the aircraft components. Fuel, being fluid, is moved in the direction of the opposing force, and in a dive at high speed the fuel may be momentarily thrown to the top of the float chamber. This interferes with the normal fuel flow with the result that the engine runs erratically or may even stop. Various 'anti-G' devices are incorporated in the carburettor design to assist in maintaining the power output of the engine while 'negative-G' conditions prevail during aerobatics; the following being typical examples of these devices.

(1) Float Needle 'Anti-G' Stop.
An adjustable stop fitted above the float needle, in conjunction with a collar on the lower end of the needle restrict the needle movement and fuel flow during aerobatics to allow only the entry of sufficient fuel to keep the engine running at maximum power conditions.

(2) 'Anti-G' Ball Valve.
A ball valve, fitted to the pressure balance vent in the float chamber, prevents fuel spillage into the choke during negative-G flying conditions.

(3) 'Anti-G' Stand Tube.
Engine cutting due to fuel starvation is precluded by a stand tube which feeds the metering jet from the centre of the float chamber.

Fig.7-10 shows the various 'Anti-G' devices as listed above in a carburettor.

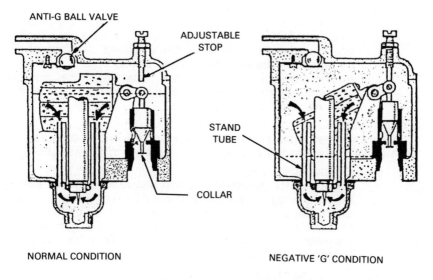

Fig.7-10. Carburettor Anti 'G' Devices.

7.4 Carburettor Heating.

(a) General.

To ensure satisfactory operation and efficient carburation some parts of the carburettor, in particular the throttle, choke and air intake, must be maintained at temperatures which will prevent the formation and accumulation of ice. Icing encountered by aircraft engines can be divided into two distinct types, carburettor icing and impact icing. Each is formed in a different manner and may occur either separately or together between atmospheric temperatures of −15C and +25C. Ice formed at temperatures below this range is of a sufficiently dry nature not to adhere and accumulate within the carburettor or around the air intake.

  (i) Carburettor Icing.

       The construction in the induction system caused by the choke and the throttle valve not only cause an increase in the velocity and a decrease in the pressure of the induced air, but also lower the temperature. Furthermore, as heat is required to convert a liquid into a gas, the fuel which vaporises in the induction system absorbs heat from the induced air and the surrounding metal, resulting in an additional drop in temperature. When the temperature of the air is reduced to below 0C the moisture content in the air begins to precipitate and form as ice. The added constriction caused by the ice formation results in an increasing air velocity and a progressive lowering of the temperature. With these conditions ice builds up more rapidly in the system causing loss of engine power, rough running and jamming of the throttle valve.

(ii) Impact Icing.
This form of icing occurs most readily at temperatures between 0C and −7C and is caused by rain droplets turning into ice on striking the exposed surfaces of the carburettor. The ice adheres and builds up around the air intake disturbing the airflow, upsetting the mixture strength and resulting in rough running and loss of power and may even stop the engine.

(b) Protection Against Ice.
The various methods and devices used to prevent or disperse ice formation in and around the carburettor are described as follows:

(i) Gapped Ice Guards.
A gapped ice guard consists of a wire screen mounted a suitable distance ahead of the air intake. Should the ice guard become blocked with snow or ice, air can continue to flow into the carburettor through the gap formed between the guard and the intake. This device gives protection against impact ice.

(ii) Sheltered Air Intake.
This device is used in conjunction with the gapless type ice guard. The sheltered air intakes, which provide an alternative entry for the air, are situated within the engine cowling and are fitted with shutters operated either automatically or by electro-pneumatic rams controlled by switches in the pilot's cockpit. The automatically operated shutters are opened by the depression created in the air intake system as the gapless ice guard becomes blocked with ice. Additionally the sheltered intake may be designed to draw its air from around heated parts of the engine or coolant radiator, thus supplying heated air to the carburettor.

(iii) Alcohol Injection System.
In some installations, in addition to the heated air system an alcohol injection system is incorporated and is used as an emergency method of dispersing ice which may form in spite of the use of the warm air system. The system comprises an electrically driven or hand operated pump delivering alcohol from a small supply tank to the jets, positioned in the carburettor air intake which direct the spray of spirit toward the throttles. Generally the supply of de-icing spirit is sufficient for ten to fifteen minutes continuous operation at the maximum delivery rate.

(iv) Heated Throttles and Throttle Housings.
Carburettor icing is best prevented by circulating hot oil from the engine scavenge system, through jackets surrounding the throttle bores, and through the hollow spindles and throttle valves. This method in conjunction

with a controlled heated air supply for the air intake is usually adequate and does not require the addition of a de-icing spirit injection system.

Note: The operational effects of carburettor heating are explained in Chapter 10.

7.5   Injection Carburettors.

The Stromberg injection carburettor differs from the previous carburettors in that it is not fitted with a float chamber nor does the choke depression act directly on the jets. The choke is known as the large venturi and inside it a small or boost venturi is fitted; this has the effect of lowering the pressure still further and this depression in the boost venturi acts upon a diaphragm which in turn regulates the flow of fuel into the carburettor by means of a poppet valve. The fuel is discharged through a spray nozzle fitted near to the eye of the supercharger. This arrangement has the following advantages:

(a)   The amount of fuel passing through the jet is dependent on the pressure inside the carburettor and is therefore almost unaffected by aerobatics and 'negative' 'G' conditions.

(b)   The spray nozzle helps to atomise the fuel.

(c)   Fuel under pressure reduces the liability of vapour locks.

(d)   There is no vaporisation and consequent cold spot around the jet mouths; this helps to prevent ice formation.

Note: In this type of carburettor, the choke is retained purely as a means of measuring the airflow.

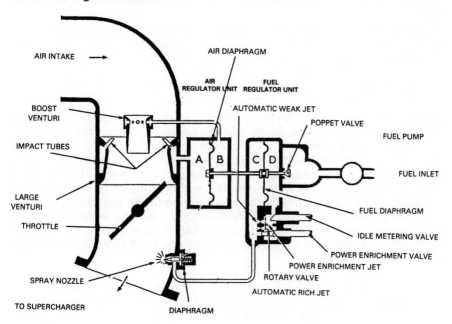

Fig.7-11. Fuel Injection Carburettor.

7.6 Fuel Injectors.

Fuel injectors differ fundamentally from float-type and injection carburettors in that the airflow to the engine is not measured by a venturi. They are thus, strictly speaking, not carburettors but engine driven pumps which supply fuel direct to the cylinders via the supercharger or turbocharger in accordance with engine requirements. Below is the description and basic operation of a typical fuel injector:

Fig.7-11 is a diagram of a fuel injector which is fitted in place of the standard engine fuel pump, and which also performs all the functions of a normal aircraft carburettor. The air supply to the engine is controlled in the usual way by a throttle valve in conjunction with a boost control unit not shown in the diagram. Fuel is forced into the governor chamber by the vane type feed pump, which is designed to supply an excess, so that surplus fuel escapes through the relief valve and the pressure in the governor chamber remains constant.

Rotation of the governor causes the needle valve to be opened and fuel flow, first into the governor chamber, and then through the two variable jets into the metered fuel chamber. The difference in pressure between the governed and metered fuel chambers acting on the diaphragm tends to close the needle valve in opposition to the action of the governor. Now, as the thrust exerted by a centrifugal governor is proportional to the square of the rpm and as the diaphragm always balances that thrust, it will be realised that the pressure difference across the diaphragm is also proportional to the square of the rpm. Consequently, as the flow of fuel through a jet is proportional to the square root of the pressure difference across it, for a given opening of the jets the fuel flow through them will vary directly with the engine speed.

The pressure in the governor chamber being higher than that in the governed fuel chamber, there is a small residual pressure on the needle valve tending to close it. This is balanced out by the "idle" spring fitted against the outer surface of the diaphragm. The spring load is adjustable providing a means of varying the fuel flow at idling conditions, when the thrust from the governor is very small.

The flow of fuel through the main jet (at a given rpm) is governed by the boost pressure and the exhaust back pressure. Ignoring the latter, for the moment, the effect of an increase in boost is to compress the evacuated boost pressure capsules, this causing the main metering needle to withdraw and the flow of fuel through the jet to increase. Control of mixture strength to suit all operating conditions is effected by variation in the taper of the main metering needle, so that the rich/weak/rich characteristic is automatically provided over the whole range of boost pressures from idling to take off. As the flow of fuel is governed by boost and rpm, no altitude control of the kind fitted to float type carburettors is required.

It will be recalled that the fall in air pressure with altitude, results in less exhaust gas remaining in the cylinders at the end of each exhaust stroke and, consequently, the volumetric efficiency improves, i.e. more mixture goes into each cylinder at a given induction pressure. In the

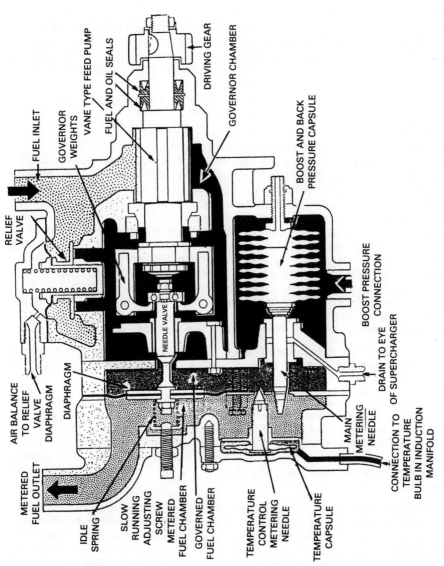

Fig.7-12. Fuel Injection Pump Unit.

float type carburettor the extra fuel is automatically drawn off by the increased depression in the choke, but in a fuel injector, compensation is necessary to avoid weakening of the mixture.

Here compensation is provided by the back pressure capsule, which although integral with the boost pressure capsule, is sealed from it and subjected to atmospheric pressure. Thus, as height is gained the back pressure capsule is compressed and the main metering needle is withdrawn sufficiently to maintain a constant mixture strength. To ensure that the main metering needle responds accurately to capsule movement, it is essential for it not to be a tight fit in its supporting bushes. Consequently, to prevent leakage between the boost and governed fuel chambers, a drainage channel is provided between the bushes.

The introduction of a temperature correction unit to the metering system is necessitated by the fact that, for a constant boost pressure and rpm, the mass airflow through the engine falls as the temperature rises, because of the reduced density of warmer air. As any decrease in airflow must be accompanied by a proportional drop in fuel consumption to maintain a constant mixture strength a temperature controlled auxiliary jet is added in parallel with the main jet. Control is effected by the single capsule unit, which is coupled to a thermometer bulb located in the induction manifold by a capillary tube, the system normally being filled with turpentine. When the mixture temperature rises, either because of a change in outside air temperature or through a change from low to high supercharger gear, the resulting expansion of the turpentine causes the capsule to compress and the attached metering needle to reduce the fuel flow through the auxiliary jet.

From the injector the metered fuel is delivered to the injection nozzle at the supercharger inlet via the accelerator pump and flexible hose, see Fig.7-12.

To maintain a constant discharge pressure, irrespective of the rate of fuel flow, a needle valve, controlled by a spring loaded diaphragm, is included in the nozzle assembly. When the metered fuel pressure rises to approximately 6lb/sq in the valve diaphragm is forced outwards, thereby opening the valve against the action of the spring. The greater the fuel flow the more will the diaphragm be deflected and the valve opened.

The diaphragm spring chamber is connected by a tube to the air intake via a slow running cut out device which, when operated, cuts off the air balance connection and admits fuel at pump pressure to the rear of the diaphragm. As soon as the diaphragm spring chamber is filled, the diaphragm is forced inwards and the needle valve thereby closed. When the cut off control is released the air balance connection is restored and fuel from the chamber drains to the air intake.

The accelerator pump shown in Fig.7-12 is simply a diaphragm operated by the throttle lever. When the throttle is opened the diaphragm is forced in (to the left) and the flow of fuel to the nozzle is temporarily increased.

7.7   Fuel Cut-Off.

A pilot operated fuel cut-off is fitted to most injectors: it cuts off all fuel irrespective of the throttle setting. However some types of injector have a cut-off which functions only when the throttle is closed.

TEST YOURSELF 7
CARBURETTORS AND INJECTORS

1. An alternative name sometimes given to the choke is the:
   (a) butterfly.
   (b) venturi.
   (c) intake controller.
   Ref. Para 7.2. Fig.7-1.

2. As engine speed is increased:
   (a) excessive fuel is prevented from passing through the main jet by the diffuser.
   (b) excessive fuel is prevented from passing through the main jet by the pressure duct.
   (c) the variable jet increases fuel supply with altitude.
   Ref. Para 7.3(b). Fig.7-3.

3. During take off, to assist in achieving maximum permissible engine power:
   (a) the accelerator pump is operated continuously.
   (b) the diffuser is fully open.
   (c) the enrichment jet supplies a very rich mixture.
   Ref. Para 7.3(e). Fig.7-6.

4. When some types of aircraft are in inverted flight, fuel starvation of the engine is avoided by:
   (a) the enrichment jet.
   (b) the fitting of a stand tube to the float chamber.
   (c) the diffuser.
   Ref. Para 7.3(i). Fig.7-10.

5. The carburettor cut-out, if fitted, is normally:
   (a) attached to the diffuser.
   (b) located in the slow running jet line.
   (c) pressure balance duct.
   Ref. Para 7.3(h). Fig.7-9.

6. To prevent fuel starvation due to sudden opening of the throttle:
   (a) the enrichment jet is fitted.
   (b) the pressure balance duct is fitted.
   (c) the accelerator pump is fitted.
   Ref. Para 7.3(f). Fig.7-7.

7. To ensure a smooth rate of discharge of fuel from the carburettor jet:
   (a) a balance duct is fitted.
   (b) a twin jet is fitted.
   (c) the float chamber is subjected to boost pressure.
   Ref. Para 7.3(a).   Fig.7-2.

8. When an aircraft is inverted in flight, fuel starvation of the engine may be prevented by:
   (a) the carburettor balance duct.
   (b) the power jet.
   (c) a stand tube.
   Ref. Para 7.3(h).   Fig.7-10.

9. Carburettor anti-icing is normally provided by:
   (a) hot air from the cooling system.
   (b) hot oil from the engine lubrication system.
   (c) spray mat heater elements.
   Ref. Para 7.4(b).

10. In an injection carburettor, the:
    (a) fuel flow is measured by the choke.
    (b) airflow is measured by the choke.
    (c) air and fuel are mixed in the choke.
    Ref. Para 7.5.

8

SUPERCHARGING

8.1 Introduction.

The magnitude of the power developed by a piston aero engine is dependent upon the weight of fuel and air mixture burnt in the cylinders in a given time. As each piston descends on the induction stroke it creates a depression, and the weight of mixture, usually referred to as the charge, that enters the cylinder is dependent on the pressure in the induction manifold, which in a conventional or aspirated engine, is governed by the pressure of the atmosphere and the amount by which the throttle is opened. As a consequence, as the atmospheric pressure progressively decreases with increase of altitude, as the aircraft climbs, the weight of charge entering the cylinders is slowly decreasing for a given throttle setting. To prevent a loss of power as altitude is increased it is necessary to maintain the inlet manifold pressure at sea level conditions. To achieve this a supercharger may be used.

Note: An aspirated engine is a non-supercharged engine.

8.2 Supercharger.

(a) Location and drive.

A supercharger is basically an engine driven fan or impeller, sometimes termed a blower, which is normally positioned between the carburettor and the induction manifold. The supercharger is normally mounted on the rear face of the engine as shown in Fig.8-1.

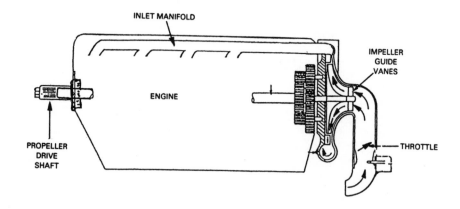

Fig.8-1. Location of Supercharger on Rear Face of Engine.

The supercharger is driven through gearing from the engine crankshaft and may be single or multi-staged.

The impeller or fan of the supercharger, normally revolves at nine to ten times faster than the engine rpm. The impeller drive absorbs an appreciable amount of horse power and to reduce the impeller bearing load it is common practice to have a three fold drive to the impeller drive shaft, i.e. three trains of gears.

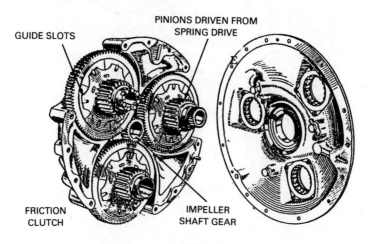

Fig.8-3a. Friction Clutch Mechanism.

An intermediate clutch that equalises the load and relieves the gearing from shock loads during sudden changes in engine speed is usually fitted with the gear trains. To smooth the drive further and so reduce vibration of the impeller, some form of spring drive is normally fitted and used as the initial drive from the crankshaft. Supercharger bearing lubrication is provided by the engine lubrication system.

Fig.8-3a shows the friction clutch mechanism used to reduce the gearing from shock loads.

Fig.8-3b shows the spring drive mechanism which may be used to reduce vibration by smoothing the drive transmission.

(b) Mixture Flow.

The fuel/air mixture is drawn through the carburettor by the supercharger and enters the eye of the impeller, the rotational speed of the impeller then throws the mixture outwards with increasing velocity to the impeller tip. Surrounding the impeller is a system of divergent passages, collectively known as a diffuser, the function of which is to smoothly decelerate the flow of the mixture on leaving the impeller to give an increase in pressure as it enters the inlet manifold. The mixture once it has entered the inlet manifold under pressure from the impeller is normally referred to as manifold pressure.

A pressure gauge situated in the cockpit, sometimes graduated in pounds per square inch, or inches of mercury, indicates the pressure above or below standard sea level atmospheric pressure. Fig.8-4 shows an example Boost Gauge (manifold pressure gauge).

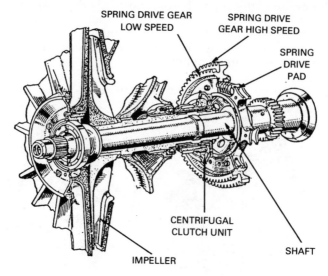

SPRING DRIVE GEAR LOW SPEED

SPRING DRIVE GEAR HIGH SPEED

SPRING DRIVE PAD

CENTRIFUGAL CLUTCH UNIT

SHAFT

IMPELLER

Fig.8-3b. Spring Drive Mechanism.

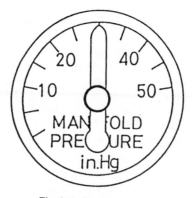

Fig.8-4. Boost Gauge.

Note: Standard atmosphere pressure is indicated as zero on the boost gauge.

8.3   Automatic Boost Control.

Pressure above normal atmospheric pressure is referred to as 'Boost Pressure or sometimes as Positive Boost' and below atmospheric pressure as 'Negative Boost'.

A boost control unit, or more commonly called automatic boost control unit, is fitted to most supercharged engines to maintain sea level atmospheric pressure in the inlet manifold as the aircraft climbs. With the increase in altitude the density of the air reduces as a result the automatic boost control unit will:

(a) be to maintain sea level atmospheric pressure in the inlet manifold by automatically controlling the throttle.

(b) be to relieve the pilot of constant boost setting adjustment for a given rpm as the aircraft climbs or descends.

(c) be to prevent the supercharger overboosting the manifold at low altitude which may result in overstressing and damage to the engine.

(d) be to control the boost pressure within certain limits to avoid mixture detonation.

(e) be to prevent excessive combustion pressures at any altitude which may lead to mechanical strain or failure.

To control the manifold pressure or boost it is necessary to restrict the opening and closing of the throttle (butterfly) by the fitting of the automatic boost control unit which adjusts the engine rpm which in turn controls the rpm of the supercharger and hence the manifold pressure. The net result of this action is control of the weight of charge entering the cylinders.

Fig.8-5 shows an automatic boost control unit with its relative position and linkage to the carburettor, throttle and supercharger.

8.4 Supercharger Automatic Boost Control Operation.

The aneroid capsule assembly is exposed only to inlet manifold or boost pressure in the induction system, in turn it is coupled to the throttle linkage via an oil operated servo piston in such a way that when the capsule is compressed the throttle or butterfly is partly closed, and when the aneroid capsule expands the throttle valve will be partly opened. The oil which operates the servo piston is supplied under pressure by the engine lubrication system.

When the engine is started the induction manifold pressure will fall to a low value, this is due to the increase in velocity of the mixture flow caused by the supercharger operation. This reduction of pressure in the inlet manifold will be sensed by the aneroid capsule assembly as it is sensitive to pressure change in the manifold, resulting in the capsules expanding. The expansion of the aneroid capsule will then cause oil to be directed below the servo piston which is moved to the top of its stroke. Subsequent throttle opening is accompanied by an increase in induction manifold pressure, causing the aneroid capsule to compress and the valve to rise until the supply of oil to the underside of the piston is cut off. Any further opening of the throttle will now cause oil to be directed above the piston, which will descend and close the throttle valve until the induction pressure falls sufficiently to cut off the servo oil supply. Therefore whatever the position of the throttle lever, the induction pressure or boost, cannot rise above a certain value, known as 'Rated Boost'.

With the valve in the equilibrium position, any tendency for the induction pressure to fall as height is gained will be counteracted by a progressive opening of the throttle or butterfly through the admission of more oil beneath the servo piston, until the altitude is reached where, with the throttle lever fully advanced, the throttle is fully open. This situation, Rated Altitude, is the point above which the induction manifold pressure will fall as with an unsupercharged or aspirated engine.

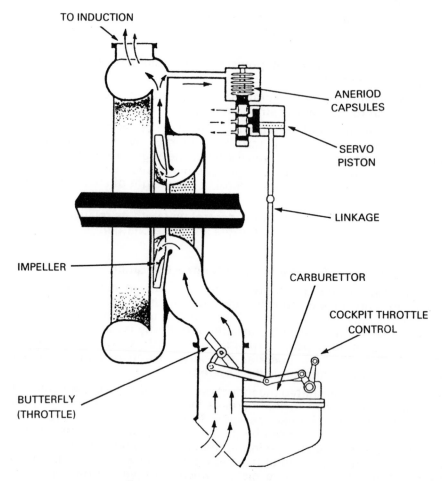

Fig.8-5. Automatic Boost Control.

8.5 Operational Example.

For the purpose of a better understanding of the relationship between the supercharger, throttle and engine rpm let us look at an example of a supercharger that is capable of a pressure ratio of 2:1.

(a) Assume the engine speed to be 2600 rpm.

(b) The impeller speed to be a ratio of 9:1 to be 23,400 rpm.

(c) Maximum take-off boost not to exceed +6lb sq in.

With the above conditions the manifold will have an absolute pressure of 20.7lb sq inch. This is 14.7lb sq inch an assumed atmospheric pressure plus 6lb sq inch boost providing 20.7lb sq inch. Such figures relate to an example of a maximum of 6lb sq inch boost.

In reality at 6lb sq inch boost pressure the throttle will be only partially open. If the throttle is fully open at sea level, with a supercharger ratio of 2:1 then the manifold pressure will be 14.7 x 2 = 29.4lb sq inch. This will exceed the maximum take off boost by 8.7lb sq inch. i.e. 29.4lb sq inch minus 20.7lb sq inch = 8.7lb sq inch.

It can be clearly seen the throttle valve must be partially closed to restrict the amount of mixture going into the manifold to keep the absolute pressure within the limitations of 6lb sq inch boost.

For the sake of simplicity at this stage there is no ram air effect as a result of forward speed on the air intake or pressure reduction due to the restriction of the carburettor. As the aircraft climbs progressively, so the density of the air reduces and the automatic boost control unit will progressively open the throttle valve to compensate for the reduction in the air density thereby maintaining 20.7lb sq inch absolute or +6lb sq inch boost in the induction manifold. This is assuming no alteration is made to the cockpit throttle setting.

When the aircraft reaches 9000ft the atmospheric pressure will now have dropped to 10.35lb sq inch therefore with a compression ratio of 2:1 the supercharger will maintain a manifold absolute pressure of 20.7lb sq inch. The automatic boost control has compensated by progressively opening the throttle up to this altitude and has now reached a position where the throttle is fully open.

As our example engine has now been maintaining constant rpm and a constant boost of +6lb sq inch we can say:

(a) With the engine set at constant rpm and constant boost with the throttle fully open it is at 9000ft or full throttle height.

(b) With the throttle fully advanced and the throttle valve fully open, the aircraft can also be said to have reached its rated altitude. If the aircraft now continues to climb above this altitude (example used 9000ft) no further compensation is available and so the manifold pressure will start to fall as it would with a normal aspirated engine.

Note: In the example given any further movement of the throttle in the cockpit, if any is still available, will in effect be lost motion as the throttle is fully open, this situation can only be changed by the fitment of a further device known as a variable datum cam.

8.6 Variable Datum Cam.

At low altitudes, the action of the automatic boost control unit, as described so far, would be such that 'rated boost', i.e. the value for that particular boost setting, would be reached with the throttle partly open, beyond which there would be lost motion on the throttle in the cockpit. Furthermore, although the aneroid capsule and unit would prevent a fall in boost pressure during a climb at full throttle, it would not be able to do so at pressure lower than the rated boost, and it would be necessary for the pilot to be continually advancing the throttle. These disadvantages are overcome by the fitting of a variable datum cam which is normally fitted to the top of the aneroid chamber of the automatic boost control unit and is interconnected with the throttle lever. Fig.8-6 shows an example of the variable datum cam assembly.

FIXED BOOST ADJUSTMENT

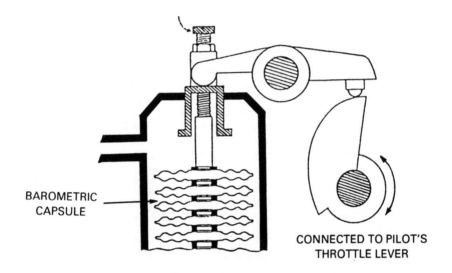

BAROMETRIC CAPSULE

CONNECTED TO PILOT'S THROTTLE LEVER

Fig.8-6. Variable Datum Cam Assembly.

Note: Barometric capsules are sometimes prone to sticking to the walls of the cylinders in which they are housed. To prevent them sticking, often a coil spring is fitted between the capsule and the cylinder wall. Such springs may also be fitted to the Automatic Mixture Control Capsule for the same reason.

8.7 Variable Datum Cam Operation.

This cam permits the aneroid unit to rise as the throttle is closed, thus, with the aneroid unit adjusted to give the rated pressure with the throttle lever fully advanced, as the throttle is closed the valve will be progressively re-set so that the equilibrium postion will occur at lower boost pressures, and for a given position of throttle lever a corresponding degree of boost will be obtained.

8.8 Full Throttle Height.

The full throttle height is the altitude up to which a given boost setting can be maintained at a given rpm.

The lower the boost pressure selected by the pilot the greater is the altitude to which it can be maintained by the automatic boost control unit. For example, in an aircraft at its rated altitude and still climbing, the butterfly will be fully open at its rated boost, which will then begin to fall; but at a lower boost the butterfly will still be opening through the action of the aneroid capsule, and the pressure will be maintained until the butterfly can open no further. This is known as 'Full Throttle Height' for that particular boost and rpm. The speed of the engine is a qualifying factor because it controls the speed of the supercharger impeller; at higher than normal rpm the full throttle height will be raised.

Note: The rated altitude is the full throttle height at rated boost and normal rpm for that boost. Fig.8-7 shows examples of power curves for a supercharged engine.

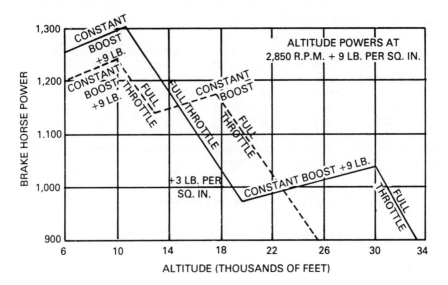

Fig.8-7. Shows Two Examples of Power Curves.

8.9 Automatic Boost Control Override.

So that the maximum possible power is available for take off and emergencies, provision is made for the rated boost to be exceeded under these circumstances. This may be done either by arranging for the pressure in the aneroid capsule chamber to be reduced through a controlled leak, or by lowering the aneroid unit beyond the rated boost position. In one installation, when the throttle lever is advanced beyond a gated position on the quadrant, an extension to the variable datum cam gives the required depression and at the same time brings the enrichment jet into operation.

8.10 Supercharger Losses.

From Fig.8-7 it will be seen that, for a constant boost and rpm setting, engine power increases up to the full throttle height. As an aircraft climbs, the fall in temperature of the air is accompanied by a corresponding drop in the charge temperature. Consequently the density of the mixture increases and a greater weight of charge is burnt per power stroke. Furthermore, the decreasing atmospheric pressure offers less resistance to the expulsion of the exhaust gases and to the downward movement of the pistons, in the former case improving the volumetric efficiency and the latter raising the mean effective pressure.

Of the total power absorbed by the supercharger a proportion is wasted in overcoming friction and in heating the mixture adiabatically. The rise in mixture charge temperature, unavoidable though it is, must be kept as low as possible because the higher the temperature the greater the loss in engine power due to reduced charge density, and the greater risk of detonation. Both friction losses and supercharger heating increase with impeller rpm; consequently for efficient operation the engine speed should be as low as possible.

It is clear that a supercharged engine is comparatively inefficient at or near sea level; much of the power absorbed by the supercharger goes to restoring the drop in induction pressure necessarily created by the butterfly to prevent over-boosting; the power developed at a given boost and rpm setting is lower than at altitude because of the higher temperature and pressure; and, although considerable power can be obtained by using high boost pressures and rpm, it involves the supply of a very rich mixture to counteract the combined effects of high air temperature and adiabatic heating.

8.11   Control Settings for Maximum Efficiency.

Maximum efficiency, or minimum specific fuel consumption, is obtained when the butterfly is fully open and the rpm is as low as can be obtained without detonation. In practice this is at the full throttle height for the power setting in use. The power is obtained by using the highest possible weak mixture boost in conjunction with the lowest practicable rpm to give the required air speed.

8.12   Two-Speed Superchargers.

When a high rated altitude is required, it is necessary to step up the supercharger gear ratio so that the impeller can be driven at a sufficiently high speed. With such an arrangement, however, the power losses at low altitudes are considerable for the reasons already given. To avoid such losses, superchargers with two impeller gear ratios are used, the change from one to the other being made either manually or automatically at a certain height. Fig.8-8 shows power curves for some example engines fitted with two speed superchargers.

Note: Superchargers with two gear ratios are normally termed two speed superchargers.

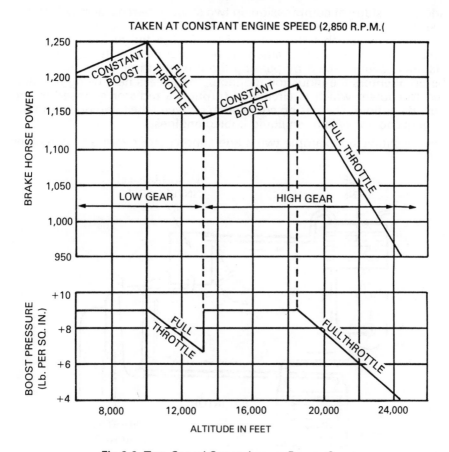

Fig.8-8. Two Speed Supercharger Power Curve.

In Fig.8-8 which shows how the power output varies with altitude at rated boost and normal rpm, the loss of power at low altitudes in high (gear 's' Fig.8-8) gear is immediately evident. Furthermore it can be seen that it is pointless to change from low (gear 'm') gear to 's' gear at the 'm' gear rated altitude for, although the rated boost pressure would be maintained, the power output would immediately fall, in this case by about 190 bhp.

The change should be delayed until the boost pressure has fallen by about 2lb sq inch, when the altitude is reached at which the 'm' and 's' power curves intersect. The rated power in 's' gear, obtained at 13,000ft, is well below that in 'm' gear because of the extra power needed to drive the supercharger at the higher speed.

On some two-speed installations the selection of high gear is automatic.

8.13 Two Stage Superchargers.

In aircraft that are required to operate at altitudes normally in excess of 30,000ft, a higher degree of supercharging than can be obtained with a two-speed impeller is needed, and it is necessary to provide an additional stage of compression. In two stage superchargers (which are also two speed) separate impeller units, mounted on a common shaft, are arranged, so that the outlet of the first is fed to the inlet of the second. The considerable adiabatic temperature rise through the two stages is counteracted by passing the mixture through an intercooler before it enters the induction manifold, the excess heat being transferred to coolant which is circulated through a radiator exposed to the outside airflow. There is no connection between the intercooler and the engine coolant system on liquid-cooled engines.

Fig.8-9 shows an example two stage supercharger with an intercooler fitted.

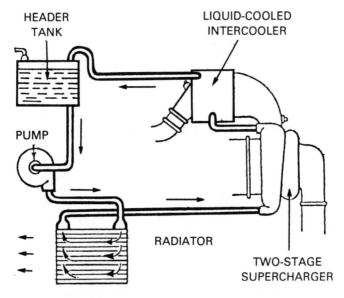

Fig.8-9. Supercharger Intercooler.

TEST YOURSELF 8
SUPERCHARGING

1. The supercharger is normally positioned:
   - (a) in the exhaust manifold.
   - (b) before the carburettor.
   - (c) between the carburettor and the inlet manifold.

   Ref. 8.2.

2. The impeller of a supercharger rotates:
   - (a) twice the speed of the engine.
   - (b) half the speed of the engine crankshaft.
   - (c) nine to ten times the speed of the engine crankshaft.

   Ref. 8.2

3. Supercharger impeller vibration may be reduced by:
   - (a) a spring drive on the impeller drive shaft.
   - (b) a spring drive on the turbine drive shaft.
   - (c) a hydro/mechanical clutch.

   Ref. 8.2

4. The supercharger is normally located:
   - (a) at the side of the engine.
   - (b) at the rear of the engine.
   - (c) at the front of the engine.

   Ref. 8.2

5. Manifold boost pressure is:
   - (a) the indicated pressure in the inlet manifold between the impeller and the inlet valves.
   - (b) the indicated pressure in the inlet prior to the carburettor.
   - (c) the pressure indicated in the supercharger.

   Ref. 8.2

9

TURBOCHARGING

9.1 Introduction.

The primary disadvantage of the supercharger is its lack of an infinitely variable drive. Much research has led in more recent years to the development and production of the turbocharger. The supercharger relies on a gear drive from the crankshaft of the engine, the turbo-charger however, utilises the exhaust gases of the engine to drive a compressor, the product of which is used to pressurise the inlet manifold in a similar manner as the supercharger. The use of exhaust gases from the engine has provided a useful source of energy in providing boost to the inlet manifold. As more than one-third of the energy that should be derived from the combustion of the fuel in the cylinders is lost through the exhaust gases, any useful work obtained from them is an asset to the performance of the engine.

9.2 Turbo-Charger Location and Drive.

The turbocharger consists primarily of a fan or compressor which is driven by a turbine which in turn is driven by the exhaust gases of the engine. See Fig.9-1.

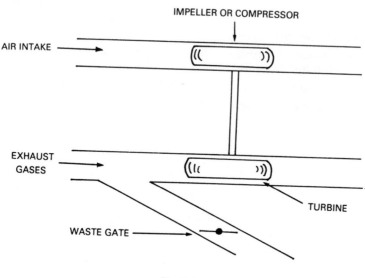

Fig.9-1.

In just the same way as the supercharger the turbocharger compressor increases the pressure in the inlet manifold thereby increasing the weight of charge of the mixture entering the cylinders. The turbo-charger turbine is located in the exhaust system and the compressor element is situated between the air intake and the carburettor or injector, unlike the supercharger which is normally positioned between the carburettor and the inlet manifold.

9.3 Example Turbocharger.

A turbocharger consists of a turbine wheel and an impeller (sometimes termed the compressor, fan or blower), fitted on a common shaft, the bearings for which are contained within a bearing housing and are lubricated by oil from the engine lubrication system. The turbine and compressor casings are attached to the bearing housing and are connected to the exhaust and intake systems respectively; the compressor is shielded from the heat of the turbine, and intake of external air is ducted between the two casings to remove excess heat. The turbocharger is not necessarily an integral part of the engine, on most engines it is not, but may be mounted on the engine or on the fireproof bulkhead, and shielded from combustible fluid lines in the engine bay.

Fig.9-2 shows an example turbocharger.

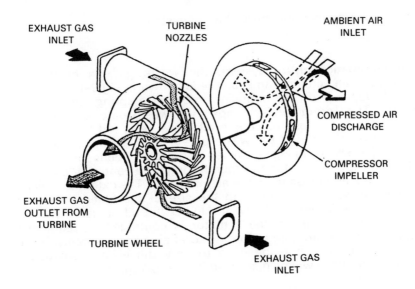

EXHAUST GAS INLET

TURBINE NOZZLES

AMBIENT AIR INLET

COMPRESSED AIR DISCHARGE

COMPRESSOR IMPELLER

EXHAUST GAS OUTLET FROM TURBINE

TURBINE WHEEL

EXHAUST GAS INLET

Fig.9-2. Turbocharger.

Engine exhaust gases are ducted to the turbine casing, where they pass through nozzles and impinge on vanes on the turbine wheel causing it to rotate; the gases then pass between the vanes and are exhausted overboard. As the impeller is attached to the same shaft as the turbine wheel it also rotates, drawing in air from the intake duct and throwing it outwards at high velocity through diffuser vanes in the compressor casing; these vanes convert the velocity energy into pressure energy, and the compressed air is delivered to the engine.

9.4 Turbocharger Operation.

For any particular power output the turbocharger delivers a fixed weight of air to the engine in a given time, and, since the density of air decreases with altitude, a greater volume of air is compressed and the impeller rotates faster at high altitude than it does at low altitude. Therefore, some form of control over compressor output must be provided, and this is achieved by varying the quantity of exhaust gas passing to the turbine. A turbine by-pass, in the form of an alternative exhaust duct, is fitted with a valve, known as the waste gate, which controls or regulates the degree of opening of the by-pass. When the waste gate is fully open nearly all the exhaust gases pass to atmosphere, but as the waste gate closes gases are directed to the turbine, and the maximum turbine speed is reached when the waste gate is fully closed. The waste gate may be manually controlled by the pilot, or more usually on modern turbochargers automatically to prevent over-boosting the engine.

Fig.9-3 shows an example turbocharger system.

In an automatic control system, the waste gate is mechanically connected to an actuator, an example is shown in Fig.9-4, the position of which depends on the opposing forces of a spring and engine oil pressure. The spring tends to open the waste gate and engine oil pressure tends to close it. Engine oil pressure is fed to the actuator through a restrictor, and the waste gate controllers are placed in the return line as shown in Fig.9-3. When a controller opens the return line, oil flows from the actuator and then through the controller back to the engine sump, and pressure in the actuator falls. The extent to which the oil pressure will fall depends on the size of the bleed through the controllers; the larger the bleed the lower the oil pressure will drop. Therefore oil pressure in the actuator is controlled to regulate the position of the waste gate according to engine requirements. Various types of controllers may be used to vary the waste gate actuator pressure, and these will be discussed in later paragraphs.

9.5 Operation of the Waste Gate.

Some simple turbocharger systems use a single controller, called an Absolute Pressure Controller, which is designed to prevent the turbocharger outlet pressure from exceeding a specified maximum; this type of controller is shown in Fig.9-4. At low power settings full oil pressure is applied to the waste gate actuator, which closes the waste gate and diverts all exhaust gases through the turbine. As the throttle is opened, engine speed increases, and more exhaust gas passes through the

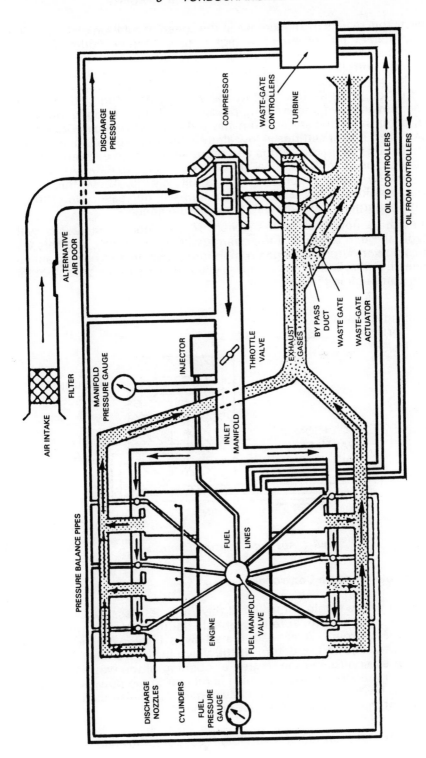

Fig.9-3. Turbocharger System.

turbine; this results in an increase in the speed of rotation of the turbine and impeller, and produces a higher turbocharger outlet pressure which is communicated to the capsule chamber in the Absolute Pressure Controller. When the controlled outlet pressure is reached, the capsule is compressed sufficiently to open its bleed valve and thus bleed off oil pressure from below the waste gate actuator piston. The piston moves down under spring pressure and starts to open the waste gate, diverting exhaust gas from the turbine and reducing its speed. Thus at high power settings at low altitude the waste gate is almost fully open, but as the aircraft climbs and more air has to be compressed it is gradually closed until, at critical altitude (equivalent to Rated Altitude on an internally driven supercharger) it is fully closed. Above this height both manifold pressure and power output will decrease, even though the turbocharger is operating at its maximum speed.

It should be noted, since the speed of the impeller increases with altitude, the temperature of the charge will also increase, and this will reduce power output for a given manifold pressure and engine speed. Engine oil and cylinder temperatures will also increase as a result of the higher combustion temperatures.

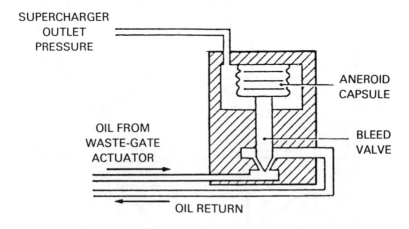

Fig.9-4. Absolute Pressure Controller.

9.6   Variable Pressure Controller.

A variation of the single controller is the Variable Pressure Controller, see Fig.9-5, which is similar to the variable datum control for internally driven superchargers. A cam, operated by a linkage to the throttle control lever, adjusts the datum of the valve in the Variable Pressure Controller, so controlling the degree of opening of the waste gate and producing a manifold pressure which is related to the power setting of the throttle lever. Operation of this system is otherwise similar to the operation of the Absolute Pressure Controller.

Fig.9-5 shows an example of a Variable Pressure Controller.

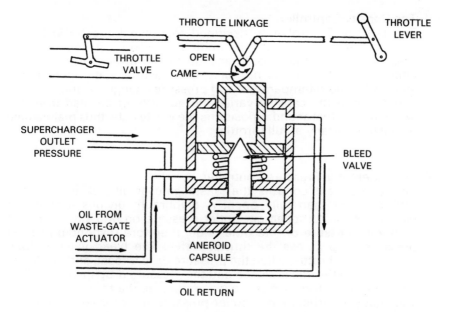

Fig.9-5. Variable Pressure Controller.

9.7 Dual Control Unit System.

On some ground boosted turbochargers a dual unit control system is used to adjust waste gate actuator oil pressure; the units are the Density Controller and the Differential Pressure Controller, which are installed as shown in Fig.9-6.

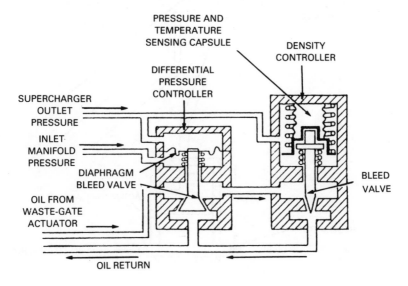

Fig.9-6. Dual Unit Controller.

(a) The Density Controller.
The Density Controller is designed to prevent the turbocharger output from exceeding the limiting pressure; it regulates oil pressure only at full throttle and up to the turbochargers critical altitude. The capsule is normally filled with dry nitrogen and is sensitive to both temperature and pressure changes. Contraction or expansion of the capsule varies the quantity of oil bled from the waste gate actuator and repositions the waste gate, thus maintaining a constant density at full throttle.

(b) The Differential Pressure Controller.
This component controls the waste gate at all positions of the throttle other than fully open. A diaphragm divides a chamber which has the turbocharger outlet pressure on one side and inlet manifold pressure on the other side, therefore responding to the pressure drop across the throttle valve. The bleed valve is fully closed at full throttle, when the pressure drop is least, and gradually opens as the throttle is closed and the pressure drop increases. The controller therefore opens the waste gate as the throttle is closed, and reduces turbocharger outlet pressure in accordance with the power selected.

Fig.9-7 shows the waste gate and its basic operation.

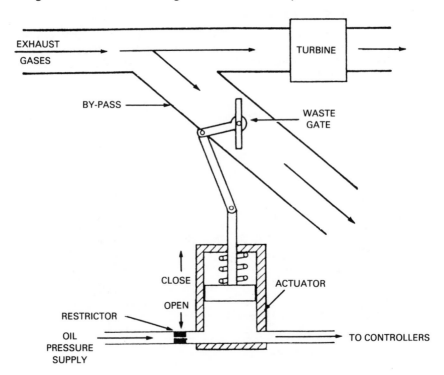

Fig.9-7. Basic Control and Operation of Waste Gate.

TEST YOURSELF 9
TURBOCHARGING

1. The waste gate of a turbocharger is normally operated, when being closed by:
   (a) spring pressure.
   (b) engine lubrication system oil pressure.
   (c) engine hydraulic system oil pressure.
   Ref. 9.4.

2. The impeller of a turbocharger of an aircraft in a climb at constant engine rpm, will:
   (a) increase with altitude.
   (b) reduce with increase of altitude.
   (c) remain constant until full throttle height is reached.
   Ref. 9.5.

3. On an aircraft flying at a specific height and constant rpm, as the throttle is then slowly closed:
   (a) the waste gate will fully close.
   (b) the waste gate will slowly open.
   (c) the waste gate will remain in the same position.
   Ref. 9.7.

4. The turbocharger impeller is situated:
   (a) prior to the fuel injector.
   (b) after the carburettor.
   (c) in the exhaust system.
   Ref. 9.2.

5. Turbocharger main bearings are lubricated by:
   (a) the engine hydraulic system.
   (b) the engine lubrication system.
   (c) grease packs.
   Ref. 9.3.

6. The turbocharger impeller is:
   (a) driven by intake ram air.
   (b) driven by exhaust gases.
   (c) mounted on the same shaft as the turbine.

   Ref. 9.3.

7. The impeller of a turbocharger:
   (a) draws air through the intake air duct.
   (b) draws air through the carburettor intake duct.
   (c) draws air through the turbine guide nozzles.

   Ref. 9.3.

8. The waste gate is:
   (a) hydraulically operated when being opened.
   (b) mechanically connected to the actuator.
   (c) electrically trimmed.

   Ref. 9.4.

9. The degree of opening of the waste gate is controlled by:
   (a) the actuator and spring.
   (b) the engine lubrication system.
   (c) the Variable Pressure Controller.

   Ref. 9.6.

10. If a leak occurs in the exhaust system prior to the turbocharger turbine, the:
    (a) waste gate will fail to operate.
    (b) boost pressure will be reduced.
    (c) the waste gate will open.

    Ref. 9.4.

10

PISTON AERO-ENGINE OPERATION AND PERFORMANCE

10.1 Introduction.

This chapter is primarily devoted to supercharged engine types driving a propeller fitted with a constant speed unit.

10.2 Precautions Before Engine Starting.

Before starting the engine the following points should be noted in respect of supercharged piston engines.

(a) Cooling.
If practicable the aircraft should be positioned facing into wind to achieve the best possible cooling from the air when the engine is running.

(b) Hydraulicing.
If the engine has been standing without being run for some time, the engine should be turned over, preferably by hand, for at least two revolutions of the propeller in order to break down the film of oil which will have formed on the cylinder walls of the engine.

If the engine is of the inverted or radial type it is possible oil may drain past the piston rings and collect in the combustion chambers of the inverted cylinders. Attempting to start the engine or engines, in this condition may create hydraulic shocks, known as hydraulicing, of a magnitude sufficient to cause serious damage to the engine. To avoid hydraulicing the propeller should be turned through two complete revolutions in order to eject the collection of oil from the combustion chambers through the exhaust manifold. If resistance is felt to turning the propeller it may be necessary to remove the sparking plugs to drain the offending oil before the propeller can be turned.

(c) Static Boost.
Whilst the engine is static, with the aircraft on the ground, prior to starting the engine the boost gauge should be read. The indicated boost in this situation is termed 'STATIC BOOST'. It is important the indicated static boost reading be noted and remembered.

The boost gauge will read the pressure that exists in the inlet manifold with the engine stationary. If the pressure in the manifold is mean sea level atmospheric pressure of 14.7lb/sq inch or 1013 millibars, then the boost gauge will read 'zero'. As atmospheric pressure varies it may read above or below zero. Whatever the indicated reading is on the boost gauge, in these conditions, it is termed 'STATIC BOOST'.

Static boost should be studied in conjunction with 'Reference Revolutions'.

(d) Engine Priming (Manually).
The fuel lines to the engine should be fully primed, that is to say, filled with fuel prior to engine starting. On engines fitted with conventional carburettors, priming is normally carried out by the operation, in the cockpit, of a hand operated fuel priming pump which is normally of a plunger type. See Fig.10-1. The pump simply draws fuel from the fuel system and sprays fuel direct, through small jets, into the inlet manifold by-passing the carburettor.

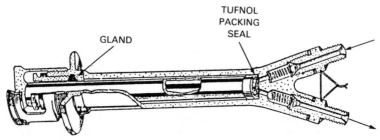

Fig.10-1. Hand operated Priming Pump.

The plunger of such pump types, must not be left out, or extended, when the engine is being started. On completion of priming the plunger must be pushed fully in and secured. Failure to secure the plunger, with it fully extended will result in fuel being drawn through the pump when the engine is started, and supplied direct to the inlet manifold. This action coupled with the fuel/air mixture being drawn through the carburettor will result in a very rich mixture at the cylinder inlet valves and will probably result in the engine stalling. Hand operated priming pumps should be operated in accordance with the aircraft manual, normally however, the pump is operated until resistance is felt.

(e) Engine Priming (Electrically).
The fuel lines to the engine should be fully primed in the same way as the manually primed system. In the electrically primed system the manually operated pump is replaced by an electrically driven pump operated by a switch or push button in the cockpit. On engines fitted with fuel injection systems priming is achieved with an electrically operated system. Such systems normally require an electrically operated booster pump being switched on in the cockpit, the system being primed with fuel and the booster pump is then switched off before any attempt is made to start the engine.

(f) Reference Revolutions.
On starting the engine the indicated boost will fall, this is primarily

due to the increased velocity of the mixture in the inlet manifold causing a decrease in pressure. To restore the manifold pressure to that indicated at static boost, the throttle must be opened further. When the indicated boost reading is the same as at static boost, the indicated rpm is reference revolutions.

10.3 Take-off.

The boost required is normally set or selected prior to take-off. Carburettor heating must also be switched off during the take-off run unless it is absolutely essential. Failure to switch off carburettor heating will result in a loss of power.

The loss of power as a result of carburettor heating being selected is due to the reduction in air density at the carburettor intake as a result of increased temperature by the anti-icing heater. A considerable loss of power is incurred during the initial take-off run due to loss of ram air effect.

Prior to take off, the engine should be run up to at least the static boost reading (ref-revs), or to the highest boost that can be held on the brakes. The purpose of this is to clear the plugs and also clear the supercharger of any residual fuel sticking to the casing.

10.4 Engine Temperatures.

It is important to watch the engine cylinder head temperature and or coolant and oil temperatures, and keeping them within the limitations.

The cooling of air cooled cylinders is controlled by the setting of gills which in general should be:

(i)   Fully open for all ground operations, or running, provided the engine has reached normal operating temperature or +100 degrees centigrade.

(ii) Closed or part open for take-off.

(iii) Adjusted in flight as required.

If the gills or cooling ducts are closed, drag is minimised and during take-off safety speed is reached earlier. On the majority of aircraft the cowling gills are controlled by switches marked "Open", "Off" and "Close". To operate the gill motor, the switch is depressed and the gills set as required; when the desired position is reached, as shown by the gill position indicator. The switch should then be turned off.

The cooling of liquid cooled engines is in the majority of examples regulated automatically, but the pilot may have control of the air through the radiator. Radiator shutters should be open only as much as is required for adequate cooling, thus reducing the drag.

Temperatures of all types of engines can be reduced by climbing the aircraft at some 10 to 15 knots faster than the recommended climbing IAS without seriously affecting the rate of climb. Climbing with weak mixtures may lead to high temperatures.

On liquid cooled engines the oil cooler is normally incorporated in the coolant radiator assembly and control is automatic.

10.5 Mixture Setting (Manual Mixture Control).

On engines with manual mixture controls, the mixture must be set to rich before the boost is raised to a value greater than the maximum weak mixture specified.

10.6 Automatic Mixture Control.

There are two main methods of automatic mixture regulation:

(a) The throttle lever is set to give not more than the maximum weak mixture boost, therefore ensuring that the mixture is correctly set.

(b) The throttle is set at or behind the economical cruise position marked on the quadrant.

With engines using method (a) some care is necessary, particularly when flying at or near full throttle height, to ensure that rich mixture is not being used inadvertently. To ensure that weak mixture is in use under these conditions, the throttle should be opened fully and then slowly closed until the boost starts to fall; this position will then give the required weak mixture setting. If at any time the fuel consumption becomes high, a check should be made to see that weak mixture is in fact being used.

10.7 Climbing.

On most aircraft the rpm and boost are automatically maintained at the values set by the pilot until the full throttle height for that power is reached. If the climb is continued above this height the boost then falls progressively.

10.8 Some Common Faults.

(a) On engine starting, black smoke is seen coming from the exhaust manifold:

Mixture too rich.

(b) On engine starting, blue smoke is seen coming from the exhaust manifold:

Oil leaking into the combustion chamber past the piston rings.

(c) On engine starting, black smoke is seen coming from the exhaust manifold, mixture setting is correct, throttle setting is correct:

Engine is overprimed.

Manual priming pump has not been locked and is allowing additional fuel into the inlet manifold.

(d) Engine idle rpm is difficult to maintain for the correct throttle setting:

VP Prop ground fine, or extra fine has not been selected.

(e) During ground running engine temperature rises above normal:

Engine cooling gills or shutters are fully closed or not in the recommended position.

(f) During taxying the engine tends to overheat:

Engine cooling gills or shutters in closed position, normally, should be kept in fully open position during taxying.

(g) During take-off, a loss of power is experienced for a given rpm and boost.

Carburettor warm air is selected. During take-off this should only be selected if it is absolutely necessary.

(h) A backfire occurs during starting on an aircraft with an updraught carburettor:

Warm air is selected, this must be avoided or it may result in priming fuel igniting and causing a serious fire.

(i) When throttling back (closing throttle), for example on final approach, engine "backfires" coupled with a rapid rise in inlet manifold pressure.

Throttle is closed too quickly causing boost reversal.

(j) When descending from altitude, in an aircraft fitted with automatic boost control, boost pressure rises excessively.

Waste gate is possibly seized in the closed position. Engine must be controlled on the throttle to reduce the overboosting.

PRACTICE PAPER 1

1. The "Otto" cycle is:
   (a) induction, power, compression, exhaust.
   (b) compression, induction, power, exhaust.
   (c) exhaust, induction, power, compression.
   (d) compression, power, exhaust, induction.

   Ref. Ch. 2   Para 2

2. The compression ratio of a piston engine is:
   (a) a ratio of volumes.
   (b) a ratio of areas.
   (c) a ratio of pressures.
   (d) a ratio of area and volume.

   Ref. Ch. 2   Para 3

3. The inlet valve of a piston engine:
   (a) opens after top dead centre to ensure maximum weight of charge is induced.
   (b) opens before top dead centre to ensure maximum weight of charge is induced.
   (c) opens after the exhaust valve to ensure fire in the inlet manifold is avoided.
   (d) opens before the exhaust valve closes to reduce the temperature in the exhaust manifold.

   Ref. Ch. 2   Para 6a

4. The primary function of duplicated valve springs is to:
   (a) provide a back up spring if one should break.
   (b) ensure a gas tight seal is made between valve and valve seat.
   (c) minimise valve bounce.
   (d) increasing cooling surfaces.

   Ref. Ch. 2   Para 10

5. The camshaft of a piston engine rotates:
   (a) at the same speed as the crankshaft.
   (b) at twice the speed of the crankshaft.
   (c) at four times the speed of the crankshaft.
   (d) at half the speed of the crankshaft.

   Ref. Ch. 2   Para 11

6. As the piston is forced down the cylinder on the power stroke:
   (a) the gas temperature will increase.
   (b) the gas pressure will progressively increase.
   (c) the gas temperature will reduce.
   (d) the gas temperature and pressure will remain constant.
   Ref. Ch. 2   Para 3c

7. The space above the oil in a dry sump lubrication system oil tank:
   (a) is to allow for oil displacement by the pressure pump control piston.
   (b) is to allow for oil expansion and frothing.
   (c) provides for tank pressurisation.
   (d) allows for scavenge pump ram displacement.
   Ref. Ch. 3   Para 5

8. The output pressure of the pressure pump of a dry sump lubrication system is controlled by:
   (a) a relief valve.
   (b) the movement of the swash plate.
   (c) the operation of the scavenge pump.
   (d) the pressure plate displacement piston.
   Ref. Ch. 3   Para 5c

9. In a dry sump lubrication system:
   (a) return oil is collected direct from the oilways by the scavenge pump.
   (b) return oil drains into the sump and is then scavenged.
   (c) the engine sump is eliminated to save weight.
   (d) oil is fed direct to the bearings and returned direct to the tank.
   Ref. Ch. 3   Para 5h

10. The scavenge pump:
   (a) has a lower pumping capacity than the pressure pump.
   (b) normally is of a swashplate design.
   (c) scavenges at the same rate as oil is pumped into the system.
   (d) has a greater pumping capacity than the pressure pump.
   Ref. Ch. 3   Para 5h

11. Aircraft piston engine lubrication systems are:
   (a) are normally of the wet sump type.
   (b) are normally of the dry sump type.
   (c) are of a sumpless type.
   (d) are of a compound lubrication type.
   Ref. Ch. 3   Para 5

12. The by-pass valve in a dry sump lubrication system is:
    (a) to allow oil to by-pass the sump when maximum pressure is reached.
    (b) to allow oil to by-pass the filter when the element is blocked.
    (c) to allow oil to by-pass the auxiliary system until normal operating temperature is reached.
    (d) to allow oil to by-pass the cooler.
    Ref. Ch. 3   Para 5

13. A condenser is fitted to the distributor to:
    (a) minimise arcing at the points.
    (b) reduce the speed of collapse of the magnetic field.
    (c) intensify arcing at the points.
    (d) control and direct the high tension impulses.
    Ref. Ch. 4   Para 7e

14. On a four stroke engine the spark will occur:
    (a) once each revolution.
    (b) twice each revolution.
    (c) once every two revolutions.
    (d) four times each revolution.
    Ref. Ch. 4   Para 10

15. In flight, if the mixture weakens, for efficiency, the ignition timing should be:
    (a) advanced.
    (b) retarded to TDC.
    (c) retarded to before TDC.
    (d) unaltered.
    Ref. Ch. 4   Para 19c

16. Vapour locks are prevented from forming in fuel system pipelines by:
    (a) the main fuel pump.
    (b) ram air fuel tank pressurisation.
    (c) the fitting of booster pumps.
    (d) swash plate pumps.
    Ref. Ch. 5   Para 7a

17. Booster pumps are:
    (a) mechanically driven and electrically selected.
    (b) electrically driven.
    (c) air driven for safety.
    (d) driven by the hydraulic system.
    Ref. Ch. 5   Para 7a

18. The engine fuel pressure warning light flickers in flight:
    (a) the booster pump should be switched on.
    (b) the collector pump should be switched on.
    (c) the main fuel pump should be switched on.
    (d) the booster pump should be switched off.
    Ref. Ch. 5   Para 7

19. The pressure balance duct of a basic carburettor is:
    (a) connected between the carburettor intake and the float chamber.
    (b) providing a pressurised (above atmospheric) space above the fuel in the float chamber.
    (c) connected between the diffuser and the float chamber.
    (d) connected between the choke and the float chamber.
    Ref. Ch. 7   Para 3a

20. When the throttle is opened rapidly, additional fuel is supplied to the engine by:
    (a) the choke jet.
    (b) the enrichment jet.
    (c) the accelerator pump.
    (d) the power jet.
    Ref. Ch. 7   Para 3f

21. A supercharger is normally located:
    (a) prior to the carburettor.
    (b) between the carburettor and the inlet manifold.
    (c) in the exhaust manifold.
    (d) in the exhaust manifold by-pass duct.
    Ref. Ch. 8   Para 2

22. Vibration in a supercharger may be reduced by:
    (a) a spring drive mechanism.
    (b) a friction clutch.
    (c) hydraulic drive.
    (d) mechanical overload diffusers.
    Ref. Ch. 8   Para 2

23. When the engine is started on a supercharged engine, manifold pressure will:
    (a) rapidly rise.
    (b) slowly rise.
    (c) remain constant.
    (d) fall.
    Ref. Ch. 8   Para 4

24. A given boost, can be maintained at a given rpm up to an altitude which is known as:
    (a) critical height.
    (b) rated boost altitude.
    (c) rated throttle height.
    (d) full throttle height.

    Ref. Ch. 8   Para 8

25. An intercooler is sometimes fitted between the supercharger and inlet manifold:
    (a) to reduce pre-ignition.
    (b) to minimise detonation.
    (c) to reduce the weight of charge.
    (d) to increase the combustion temperature.

    Ref. Ch. 8   Para 13

26. The impeller of a supercharger rotates at:
    (a) twice the speed of the crankshaft.
    (b) four times the speed of the crankshaft.
    (c) twenty times the speed of the crankshaft.
    (d) nine to ten times the speed of the crankshaft.

    Ref. Ch. 8   Para 2

27. The impeller of a turbocharger:
    (a) reduces rpm with increase of altitude.
    (b) rotates at a constant rpm with variations of altitude controlled by the waste gate.
    (c) increases rpm with increase of altitude for a given waste gate setting.
    (d) will reduce rpm with increase of altitude as the waste gate closes.

    Ref. Ch. 9   Para 4

28. A turbocharger's rpm is regulated by:
    (a) the waste gate.
    (b) the impeller rpm.
    (c) hydraulic system oil pressure.
    (d) spring pressure.

    Ref. Ch. 9   Para 4

29. As the throttle is being closed, when the aircraft is flying straight and level at altitude, the waste gate will:
    (a) remain fully open.
    (b) move to the fully closed position.
    (c) move towards the open position.
    (d) remain in the same position.

    Ref. Ch. 9   Para 7

30. On engine starting, the waste gate will:
    (a) move toward the closed position.
    (b) remain fully open.
    (c) remain in the same position as that prior to starting.
    (d) move to the fully closed position.

    Ref. Ch. 9   Para 10